Lucilla Andrews was born in Suez, the second daughter of an English father and a Spanish mother. Her late father was then a manager in the Eastern Telegraph Company. At three she began her education in an English private girls' boarding school in Sussex and when she was eleven she wrote her first novel — an epic of love, lust and banditry in China. Unfortunately the manuscript was discovered and ended in the school incinerator.

During World War II, Lucilla Andrews entered the Nightingale Training School at St. Thomas's Hospital in London and five years larer left with an S.R.N. and S.C.M. Part One. She married a doctor, had one child, and when her husband's illness necessitated that she become the family breadwinner she returned to nursing.

Her first book, THE PRINT PETTICOAT, was written while she was working as an assistant Night Sister in a small Sussex hospital. Since that time it has never been out of print.

Over the years Lucilla Andrews has established herself as one of Britain's leading popular novelists. She has created what is virtually a new genre — the hospital romance — written against an authentic and detailed medical background which is drawn from her own experience.

Readers who would like to know more about Lucilla Andrews are recommended to read her autobiography, NO TIME FOR ROMANCE, an account of her life and training as a nurse in wartime London.

Lucilla Andrews lives in Edinburgh.

Also by Lucilla Andrews

MY FRIEND THE PROFESSOR
HOSPITAL CIRCLES
AFTER A FAMOUS VICTORY
IN AN EDINBURGH DRAWING ROOM
A WEEKEND IN THE GARDEN

and published by Corgi Books

A Hospital Summer

Lucilla Andrews

CORGI BOOKS

A HOSPITAL SUMMER
A CORGI BOOK 0 552 08541 3

Originally published in Great Britain
by George G. Harrap & Co Ltd.

PRINTING HISTORY
George G. Harrap edition published 1958
George G. Harrap edition reprinted 1959
Corgi edition published 1960
Corgi edition reprinted 1963
Corgi edition reissued 1967
Corgi edition reissued 1970
Corgi edition reprinted 1971
Corgi edition reissued 1974
Corgi edition reissued 1980
Corgi edition reissued 1986

This book is set in Plantin 9 pt.

Corgi Books are published by Transworld Publishers Ltd.,
61-63 Uxbridge Road, Ealing, London W5 5SA,
in Australia by Transworld Publishers (Aust.) Pty. Ltd.,
26 Harley Crescent, Condell Park, NSW 2200, and in New
Zealand by Transworld Publishers (N.Z.) Ltd., Cnr. Moselle
and Waipareira Avenues, Henderson, Auckland.

Made and printed in Great Britain by
Hunt Barnard Printing Ltd., Aylesbury, Bucks.

CONTENTS

For
MARNIE and BASIL

1

LIFE IN OBSERVATION

THE Sister in charge of the Observation Block that morning was new to the hospital and the Army. She had arrived in the camp yesterday afternoon on finishing her brief initiation period of military hospital life in London. She was young, good-looking, and she wore her new uniform with the efficient air of a highly trained nurse. Her name was Miss Thanet; her rank, Sister in the Queen Alexandra's Royal Military Nursing Service Reserve. Last evening Matron had shown her briskly round the Ob. Block. Mary Frantly-Gibbs and I, the two V.A.D.'s on evening duty in the Block, had decided Miss Thanet was a very pretty girl, and the answer to an M.O.'s prayer. We had reserved our judgment on her as a Sister, since, as Mary said, "The prettier they are, alas, the bitchier they get. On past showing, Clare dear, I would so much rather have had her look like the back of a bus."

The door of the hall that served the Ob. Block as duty-room, stock-room, sterilizing-room, and kitchen was wide open when Sister arrived on duty. It was on the ground floor; the early sun that was illuminating the square outside shone through the open door, and made the polish of the hall floor seem dim and drab.

The sunshine was cut off when Miss Thanet appeared in the doorway, and stopped still, surveying with patent horror the prospect before her.

The prospect was me. I was kneeling on the floor in front of the open grate at the far end of the hall, throwing dollops of floor-polish on to the collection of green twigs that one of the patients had scrounged from some garden to serve as kindling.

Miss Thanet recovered herself and walked up to me.

"Nurse—Dillon, isn't it? Nurse, what do you think you are doing?"

I said, "Good morning, Sister. Lighting the fire." I heaved on another handful of polish to show willing.

She shuddered. "Nurse Dillon. Did not Matron tell me last evening that you had been six months in this hospital?"

"Yes, Sister." I was sorry not to be able to give her my full attention, but I was too anxious about my fire, which was still only spluttering weakly. I threw on more polish.

"Nurse!" Her voice rose slightly. "Will you please get off the floor when you are talking to me? And will you please never again let me see you kneeling on the floor—and in an apron! What impression would the patients have if they saw you in this undignified position?"

I stood up, reluctantly. The last handful of polish seemed to be doing the trick, but I did not trust that fire. The grate was shockingly temperamental and if you did not watch it constantly at the early stages of lighting, even if the twigs began to flame, as now, it would produce a sudden draught and blow out the fire without conscience.

"I'm sorry, Sister," I apologized, "but you see——"

Miss Thanet tapped one elegant foot. "Please do not try to excuse yourself, Nurse. There can be no excuse for such unprofessional conduct. And just what do you think you are doing, wasting good floor-polish in this way? Do you not realize"—I braced myself, waited, and, as she was so new, it came—"that there is a war on? Stores are precious, and to be saved. And do you not also realize that it is May, a warm day, and one on which we shall certainly not require a fire?"

I dusted my apron as I listened to her, and kept one eye on my fire. I did not intend to let it go out again. I did not interrupt her lecture, because, as she had just reminded me, I had been six months in the Army, and those six months had taught me, among other things, that when authority was on a soap-box the technique was to listen in silence until authority stepped off the soap-box, and then carry on as before. Sisters had to lecture V.A.D.'s—that was their job; mine, at this moment, was to get that fire going properly; so when she finished speaking I apologized humbly. She turned away, and as her back was to me, I carefully dropped another lump of polish on to the smouldering twigs.

Unfortunately, the lump sizzled; so did Sister. She swung round. "Nurse Dillon, did you hear one word I said?"

I hesitated. I was wary about the explanation she was forcing me to make, as I knew she was not going to like being taught certain aspects of her new job by an untrained V.A.D., half a dozen years younger than herself.

At last I said, "I'm sorry, Sister, but I'm afraid we have to have a fire. I can't light the coal without wood, and these twigs are too green to burn without help."

"But this is May—and my duty-room. So will you be good enough," she demanded coldly, "to allow me to choose if I wish for a fire or not?"

I began again. "It is not just for keeping the room warm, Sister. I've got the breakfast eggs to boil; they are over there in that iron pot on the serving-table. And the milk has to be heated for the men's porridge, and the porridge warmed when it gets here. The porridge and the tea will be up soon, and we have no other means of heating anything in this Block." As she said nothing I added, "We'll need it after breakfast too, for any poultices—things like that—and to boil the kettle for the M.O.'s tea."

She seemed to have grasped only one of my points. "Poultices? You can't put a kaolin poultice on an open fire! It'll get covered in soot."

"We heat the kaolin pot in a saucepan of water and then spread it."

"Why"—it appeared that she found difficulty in speaking—"can't you heat the poultices on the lid of the sterilizer?"

I looked at her. "We haven't got a sterilizer, Sister."

"Surely we at least have a fish-kettle and a couple of 'Primuses'?"

"No, Sister."

"Then—how—do—we—sterilize?"

I nodded at the vast bottle of methylated spirits that towered over the rest of the equipment on the table marked "Surgery." "We flame everything in a large bowl." I did not tell her that had she come in a few minutes sooner she would have seen me dangerously throwing meth. at my wretched fire. I had come on duty to find the Block polish-tin empty, the green twigs soaking, and was desperate. One of the patients, a Scot called Gabriel, had come to my rescue. It was Gabriel who had produced the twigs during the night: he had the reputation of being able to scrounge anything, from anywhere, at any time, and had come back after a three-minute absence with a new tin of polish, which he had said he had got from the O.C.'s batman. Knowing the Archangel, as he was inevitably nicknamed, I did not doubt this.

Miss Thanet was temporarily speechless. She walked to the surgery table and examined the contents. "This should not be in here, with the kitchen utensils on one table beside it, and my desk with the men's papers on the other side. It must be moved to one of the bathrooms. I did not get a chance to see them last night, but the bathroom most convenient to this room will do. Will you see to it"—she swallowed—"directly you have your fire going?"

I was becoming quite sorry for the poor girl. "We haven't any bathrooms in this Block, Sister."

"No bathroom?" She drew her poise acquired in training round her like a cloak of dignity. "How many beds have we got? Isn't it seventy-two?"

"Yes, Sister." The fire was crackling now, the coal had caught; so I was able to relax and give her all my attention.

"Then how do our patients have baths? Aren't most of them up-patients and capable of bathing themselves?"

"Yes, Sister. They seldom stay in more than a few days; often less—only part of a day."

"And they do not have baths automatically on admission?"

"Officially no, Sister."

A faint smile removed the shocked expression from her eyes. "And unofficially, Nurse?"

"Sister Dirty Surgical upstairs is very good about not noticing the Ob. Block men in her bathrooms. The D.S. Block has seven bathrooms, and most of their men are bed-patients, so they can generally lend us a couple of bathrooms on the quiet."

She looked at the fire. "Would floor-polish be the unofficial official fire-lighter?"

I decided I was going to like Miss Thanet. "Yes, Sister."

She turned to me thoughtfully. "How long have you worked in this Block, Nurse?"

"Three months, Sister."

"I see." She studied her feet now. "So you must know all about the work here?"

I walked mentally round that one. "I've got used to it, Sister."

"Have you ever worked in a proper—that is, a civilian general hospital?"

"Only when I did the fifty hours' training we have to do before we can be called up as Mobile V.A.D.'s."

"Fifty hours," she echoed, and smiled properly. "I've spent less than half that in this camp. If we throw in my four years' general training to your side, I'd say we rate about equal in experience, Nurse." She was relaxing too. "I don't suppose you know this, but my original posting here was to work in the theatre. Miss Makins—isn't that the theatre Sister's name?— was due to be transferred yesterday, but her posting has been altered, and she is staying here for a while. Matron said yesterday that she expects I'll be posted overseas almost at once, and asked me to take over this Block for the time being, as I gather your Red Cross Sister who was previously in charge has gone to some Casualty Clearing Station?"

"Yes, Sister. Mrs Smith left for Rangmere yesterday morning."

"That was the place. As I was saying, I was not really intended for this Block, and before Miss Makins' posting was cancelled Matron took me all over the Acute Surgical Block. I must say that A.S. Block seemed to be adequately equipped, but this one— no doubt—has different functions. Matron only had time to take me quickly through the wards last night, and I was not able to get a proper impression of the place. I think it would be a sound scheme if you took me right round now, Nurse." She raised an eyebrow. "Incidentally, do you V.A.D.'s get called 'Nurse'?"

10

"Only by the Reserve Sisters, Sister. The Regulars call us 'Miss So-and-so.'"

She nodded as if she grasped the full meaning of what I had said. "One can understand that," she said, not unkindly. "You girls aren't nurses—you can't be; you haven't had any training."

I added more coal to my fire, hid the polish-tin for my use to-morrow morning, washed my hands in the nearest ablutions annexe, then returned to the hall to escort her round the Block.

The Observation Block consisted of six twelve-bedded wards; wards that were as neat and Spartan as the wards in military hospitals commonly are. The morning cleaning was in progress as we went round. The very few bed-patients lay amusing themselves with *Blighty* and *Razzle*; the shirt-sleeved up-patients were occupied in the traditional and orderly method in which British soldiers clean rooms. In each ward a man was pulling the beds away from the walls; one man swept the cleared space, followed by a man throwing down floor-polish, a third one was swinging a bumper (the long-handled polisher with a heavy flat head, beloved of the Army); and after the floor trio trailed a varying number of men carrying brass-polish, rags, nail-brushes, scrubbing powder, old biscuit-tins, and dirty ash-trays.

In the first ward Gabriel, in a spotless white shirt, well-creased blues—he always put them under his mattress at night —and neatly tied red tie, balanced an old biscuit-tin and cluster of rags on the palm of his good hand as he came forward to greet the new Sister about whom the men were as curious as the V.A.D.'s. "Good morning to you, Sister." He beamed at me. "We have not done the scrubbing of the locker-tops yet, Miss Dillon, but we will have them white in a wee while."

A tall, very untidy, very dark youth shuffled forward in plim-solls. Like Gabriel, the youth, whose name was Archibald, had his left arm in plaster. He stopped by Sister, smiled warmly, and uttered a long, incomprehensible sentence. The words fell like soft water from his nicotine-stained lips.

Sister said, "I'm sorry, I'm afraid I didn't quite catch what you said?" She glanced at me for assistance, but I could not help her, as I could seldom understand Archibald unless he spoke in monosyllables.

Gabriel translated willingly. "Archibald was wishing the new Sister a fine morning, and saying that he would now be doing a wee bit of brass-polishing for you, Miss Dillon."

Sister's smile was thoughtful. "Thank you." She watched a third man—another Scot, and another arm injury—washing the electric-light shades. "Do the men do all your cleaning?"

"Most of it, Sister. They're a wonderful help, as there are only three of us on days here, and often only one V.A.D. on at times."

Her expression made me feel she was letting this pass for the moment only. "How do we come to have so many orthopædic cases? Do we do any plastering?"

"No, Sister. We just get used as an overflow from the Orthopædic Block—that's the wing opposite to us across the square. These men came in last evening, and are due to go over to have their plasters changed or off this afternoon. They'll probably go out to-morrow."

"Have they been in here before? Is that how you seem to know them so well?"

Every man in the ward was listening openly to our conversation. Gabriel, emptying a nearby ash-tray, answered for me. "There's not a man in the camp as doesn't come into the Ob. Block afore he's away, Sister. Many's the time we've all been in here for a wee spell." His attention was drawn to some dust on the third lamp-shade on the right. "Hamish McAlistair, ye've left a streak of dirt on the right side of yon shade. Man, it looks awful bad from here."

Hamish McAlistair shook his head. "I canna reach it, man. Ye'll have to give me a leg up."

Archibald, the largest and possibly most good-natured man in that ward of good-natured men, came forward without a word, and stood by McAlistair. The smaller man, again one-handed, pulled a chair into position. Archiblad put one foot on the seat of the chair; McAlistair hopped cleverly and dangerously on to Archibald's knee, balanced himself with the help of his silent companion's good arm that was clamped round his own legs, and removed the offending dirt from the shade.

Sister opened her mouth as if to protest, closed it again, and waited silently until the operation was over. When both men were again on their two feet she said, "You know, you should not climb about like that. You might crack your plasters and injure yourselves. But tell me—how is it so many of you seem to have the same fractures?"

Gabriel, Archibald, and McAlistair were only too happy to explain how very easy—according to them—it was to crush your hand and forearm in a tank if you were newly mechanized, and how they and their mates were apparently in the habit of losing up to five fingers daily. Their explanations were added to by the other up-patients, who joined the little crowd round us, each with a more hideous and gory tale than the last; the whole being finally rounded up by Gabriel's repetition of the favourite camp story of the mythical staff-sergeant who lost both hands at one go. "And there he stood, Sister, with nothing but the wee stumps! And the blood was everywhere. . . . I tell ye—they say ye can still smell the blood in that machine to this very day!"

"There's only one flaw about the staff-sergeant, Sister," I told her as we moved on to the next ward, "and that is that no one in this hospital ever heard of him being admitted. But the men adore telling it. You'll hear it roughly once a week if you stay here."

She smiled slightly. "Mightn't it have happened in peacetime? This was a peace-time hospital, wasn't it?"

"Yes. The staff-sergeant in the Pack Store is an old Regular, and he told me this place was built before the first War." We were walking into the first ablutions annexe as I spoke; we walked out again, very quickly.

Sister asked, "Which war? The Crimea?"

The next ward was another hive of industry and her mouth tightened. "Don't you V.A.D.'s do any cleaning at all?"

I looked at my hands before answering. I had tried hard to save my hands. I had used countless lotions, slept in gloves, rubbed in soap after washing—none of them had been any good. Six months' scrubbing, washing, polishing, black-leading, and fire-lighting, had left their mark, and nothing I could do could get my hands clean, soft, or remove the engrimed lines of coal-dust from my index fingers. I said, "We do clean, most of the time, in the other blocks. This Block is rather a law unto itself. All the admitting and discharging that goes on every day makes a lot of extra work, and we have only a small staff, as our men aren't, technically, ill. When we V.A.D.'s aren't coping with meals, bed-making, temperatures, and the few medicines and treatments, we seem to spend the rest of the time unmaking beds and going to the Pack Stores for blues or uniforms."

She nodded, and made no other comment until we came to the last ward. She watched the men replacing the beds against the wall. "I think it's all right for men to help you girls occasionally, but I don't think it right that they should feel they have to work. After all, they are patients," she added reasonably, "and patients need to have things done for them, not the other way about. We'll have to do something about all this."

I said, "Yes, Sister," because that was what she expected me to say. I did not think she would be able to alter the routine, or alter the military tradition that regards sickness as a crime, and insists that if a soldier is fit to be out of bed he is fit to polish something. The sight of the men at their housework did not worry me as it did her, not because I agreed with the official attitude to soldier up-patients, but because in the last six months I had learnt a lot about soldiers. I knew our men were happy to have something to do to help them pass the long, empty hospital hours: that neither I nor Mary nor any V.A.D. I had ever known had ever had to ask one single man to do a job. I had never met a soldier, sick or well, who did not at some time offer

13

to "Lend you a hand with that, Nurse. Here—you give that to me. I'll shine, scrub, polish, or sweep it for you."

Our patients in the Ob. Block came in for 'observation.' Under that heading we had men admitted with tonsillitis and dermatitis, gastric ulcers and ringworm, Vincent's angina and mumps, backaches and bronchitis, colds in the head and bad feet, meningitis and malingerers. While the men waited to be sorted, diagnosed, and sent to the Block specific for their ailments they lay patiently side by side, wearing white day shirts when we ran out of night shirts, and khaki uniform shirts when we ran out of day shirts; swopping cigarettes, magazines, and stories under their breath; keeping up a constant good-humoured civility to the nurses, an equally constant grumble of the horrors of Army life, and nostalgic sighing for the lost joys of Civvy Street. Their grumbling might be incessant, but it was never serious; their behaviour to their nurses was uniformly charming and considerate. Bad language we never heard in an other-ranks ward; nor, whatever the Army text-books may say, was there ever need to maintain discipline. The men disciplined themselves magnificently.

Sister asked suddenly, "Do the men make good patients?"

I glanced back at the ward we had just left. A small rifleman who was sitting illicitly on the end of his bed lighting a still more illicit cigarette—it was 'after smoking' time—caught my eye and grinned inquiringly, as he held the match-flame away from the end of his cigarette. His grin asked clearly, "Will you be on the carpet if I do this, Nurse?"

I turned away quickly, so that Sister might not look back. "I've only really nursed soldiers, Sister, so I suppose I can't be much of a judge."

"But do you find them good patients?"

I said slowly, "Yes, I do. I should say that there may be other patients as good somewhere; I don't think there can anywhere be any better."

"You may be right," she replied indifferently, as if regretting she had asked my opinion on a nursing point about which I was too inexperienced to express a view of any value. "What's in there? Another ablutions annexe? I'd like to look at it."

We entered that last ablutions annexe more slowly, then immediately had to back out again quickly—not because all the latrines were occupied, as had happened previously, but because just as we entered the annexe the two medical orderlies who were cleaning it out emptied their buckets of disinfectant over the stone floor and swept the creosote solution towards us. Miss Thanet stepped neatly out of the way of the unattractive stream. "Is this used as a substitute for scrubbing the floor, Miss Dillon?"

The two orderlies watched her with expressionless faces, and leant on their squeegees, waiting for us to pass. I said, "Yes, Sister," and her mouth tightened primly, as it had done previously. As we walked away, she correctly preceding me, the two orderlies favoured me with a gloomy smile and the thumbs-down sign. I shook my head at them, and walked after her quickly. I did not think she rated a thumbs-down; she had to make a song and dance about hygiene and floor-scrubbing; she was a trained nurse, and I had never met a trained nurse who did not make a song and dance about both those things; but I was quite sure that if she stayed in the Ob. Block for a few weeks she would become quite human. The Ob. Block had that effect on Sisters, even on new Sisters like Miss Thanet, who arrived in the Block fresh from their beautifully equipped parent hospitals, with their minds filled with their excellent training, and professional notions that were often as unyielding as the starch in their fine new Army caps. It was impossible to remain unyielding about anything in the Ob. Block, where the patients, treatments, and Company Orders were altered daily if necessary; and where, since it was the emergency Block, you never knew for certain from one minute to another who was going to come in, or what was going to happen next. It was an interesting, occasionally infuriating, often frustrating, and always exciting Block in which to work; although it was considered a hard-working Block for V.A.D.'s, it was very popular with us. Mary Frantly-Gibbs and I were considered very favoured to have been in the Block for three months; Janice Sims, the third untrained member of the nursing staff, who had only been four weeks in the hospital, was constantly being asked by our fellow-V.A.D.'s which string she had managed to pull to get this Block as her first post. Janice, being new to all hospitals, accepted the irregularities of our working day as happenings common to hospital ward life; she had no ingrained professional ideas to be disorientated as poor Miss Thanet's were now being disorientated. When she and I returned to the hall after our round Miss Thanet sat down at the improvised desk and read through the report-book, looking as if she did not know what had hit her. She was due to be hit a good many times more, if she only stayed with us a couple of weeks, and when she was posted elsewhere no Army hospital would ever surprise her again.

She looked up from her reading. "Why do you use your hands to put on the coal?"

"I want to make a nest of coal," I explained, balancing each piece of the precious fuel carefully. "We haven't any tongs, and if I just shove it on from the bucket too much'll fall out, and the whole thing will collapse. If I do it this way I can get a strong basis for the cooking-pots. Like this." I put the egg saucepan in position. "And this." The double milk saucepan. "Then they'll cook while I go and wash my hands."

She said, "You should have joined the Boy Scouts instead of the Red Cross," and returned to her report-book.

When I got back from washing she was waiting to ask me another question. "What's N.D.K.? Every other man has that as a diagnosis."

"No Diagnosis Known. Sometimes there's a 'Y' added—Yet."

"A variation on P.U.O. [Pyrexia of Unknown Origin]?"

"Sometimes, not often, as they don't necessarily have a 'P'. This is a low-grade Block."

She grinned. "You are telling me, Nurse."

I smiled at her bent head and continued with my breakfast preparations, feeling very bucked at my discernment. On the whole I was a pretty bad judge of character; it was enchanting to discover that occasionally I could be right. She was not going to be bad at all; on the contrary, I thought she might be good fun to work under.

The one splendid piece of equipment the Block possessed was the clock in the hall. It was framed in ornate gilt, had a highly unmilitary appearance, kept perfect time, and announced each hour with a set of low, musical chimes. It was fixed high on one wall, and could only have its weekly winding if you stood on a table; but it was the pride of our department and the envy of all the other Blocks whose staffs frequently remarked that the only correct observation ever made in the Observation Block was what time it was.

The clock was chiming eight as Mary Frantly-Gibbs arrived on duty. Mary had worked late last night, as we were temporarily Sister-less, and had been given a half-hour's grace this morning as a reward from Matron's office. Mary was a tallish, sturdy young woman in her early thirties, with dramatic dark eyes, thick, dark, faintly greying hair, and the calm temperament of a person who had found what she sought from life and had no desire to seek further. She waved an amicable hand at me as she came into the hall, raised a dark eyebrow at Miss Thanet's back, deposited her cloak and gloves on the chair behind the kitchen table that served as our hat-stand. "Morning, Sister," she murmured, passing the desk on her way to the front of the kitchen table. Once there she took up a large wooden tray and began setting it with white china mugs.

Sister's head jerked up, and her back stiffened. "What are you doing, Nurse Frantly-Gibbs?"

"Setting a tray, Sister," returned Mary politely, jamming in another mug.

Miss Thanet closed the report-book. "When you come on duty in future"—she glanced at me to show that I was included

16

in this—"will you be kind enough to ask me first what work I wish you to do?"

Mary smiled affably. "Yes, Sister," and laid a second tray.

Miss Thanet took a deep breath. "I feel I must tell you both—although I cannot really see why it should be necessary—that I see no reason why this department should not be run as a proper hospital ward, and I intend to run it so. As I understand I am responsible for the work you V.A.D.'s do, I intend to draw up work-lists and daily routines and hope you will all be good enough to keep to my instructions." She looked round. "Shouldn't there be three of you? What's happened to the other V.A.D.?"

Mary explained that Janice was off until one. "It's her half-day, Sister. Mrs Smith gave her a morning instead of an afternoon, as Sims lives near and can get home for one night that way."

"I see." Miss Thanet did not look at all pleased with this intelligence. "Right. Will you please help Miss Dillon with the men's breakfasts, and when they are cleared will you both report to me again, and I will tell you what I want done next?"

Mary and I avoided each other's eyes, and in our best scum-of-the-earth voices chanted, "Yes, Sister. Certainly, Sister!" as the cookhouse orderly banged on the door.

"Morning, ladies!" He stomped in, dumped on the hearth one of the two large covered buckets he was carrying, then staggered off to the wards with the other. " 'Ere y'are, Jock!" we heard him greet Gabriel. "Put down yer 'arp and get started 'anding round the Rosy Lee, will ye, mate? Ta."

Sister came over to the hearth to examine the porridge. "It's half cold."

"The cookhouse is a good way from this Block, Sister," said Mary fairly. "We have to reheat nearly all the food that comes across."

"Then what about their tea? Shouldn't you heat that too?"

We assured her that despite the distance from the cookhouse the tea would be very hot. "And strong and sweet," added Mary. "The troops will stand a lot, but they won't stand bad tea. If the cookhouse dared send over lukewarm dish-water there'd be a mutiny, and no cookhouse orderly would dare show his face in the wards for fear of being lynched. That's why it's always safe to let the tea go straight in. I don't know how they keep it piping hot when everything else gets cold; I only know that it'll be piping hot."

Miss Thanet tapped her foot in answer and walked off to the wards—we guessed to investigate the tea herself. "Blimey, Clare," said Mary gently. "We're going to be learned."

I told her the opinion I had already formed of our new

17

Sister. "She's got a sense of humour"—I bailed out the eggs as I spoke—"I think it's only that she's pretty young, and takes her job seriously."

Gabriel, having delegated the tea to some other man, had come to help with the cooking. He took the eggs from me and arranged them neatly on a large plate. "It's always the young ones that give the most trouble, Miss Dillon. An old N.C.O. may wink his eye whiles; a good young one, never. Would the Sister be new to the Army?"

"First day here, anyway," replied Mary. "Hey, wait a moment with those eggs, Gabriel. The porridge isn't done yet."

"Och, the lads can eat backward, Mrs Frantly-Gibbs. It's no matter to them. But we'll be needing more help." He put two fingers in his mouth and whistled expertly. Archibald answered that whistle immediately. "Archibald, will you be taking the eggs, man? I'll be waiting on Miss Dillon. The porridge is not yet done."

Archibald said with unusual clarity, "Ye'll no' be calling yon porridge, mon!" He beamed at us as if he had made a brilliant crack, and shuffled off with the plate of eggs. Mary followed him with a tray of bread and butter; Gabriel crouched on his knees behind the vast pile of porridge plates he had put to warm in the grate and was turning all the time like a spit-boy, so that all sides of the plates should be heated, while I stirred the porridge hopefully and vainly, as no amount of stirring ever managed to remove the lumps.

I was dishing out the steaming porridge when the telephone rang. "Heck—I'm all messy. Why must it ring now?"

Gabriel handed me a tea-towel. "Use that for ye hands, Miss Dillon. I'll be giving it a rinse out for you after breakfast."

"Bless you, Gabriel—and keep that porridge steady, will you? It's about to topple over." I answered the 'phone. "Observation."

A voice that belonged to Corporal Jenkins, the N.C.O. in charge of the switchboard, inquired laconically, "Mr Slaney with you, miss?"

"Have a heart, Corporal! It's only just gone eight. Our M.O. never arrives before nine. He's not here yet."

"I reckon as he's on his way to you for all that, miss. There is," announced Corporal Jenkins grimly, "goings-on going on this morning. You not heard the news?"

"Camp or B.B.C.?" The difference lay in the fact that the camp news was always roughly two weeks ahead of the wireless bulletins; it was also remarkably accurate, which was why few of us in the camp in May 1940 ever bothered to read the newspapers—except to look at Jane—or listen to the wireless.

"Camp," he said. "There's nothing on the wireless yet, miss.

18

They was just giving out the usual this morning about everything carrying on as was expected, and moving to carefully prepared positions. What they calls strategic, miss. But we had some of the lads stop by here early this morning, and they reckon as a lot more lads'll be moving off to-day. The R.S.M., he told me not half an hour ago, he did, as he reckons there'll not be a medical orderly left in the hospital to-night. Got to move out the patients, we have, too; the M.O.'s in the major blocks are at it already fixing to shift the lads out. Got to have spare beds, we have—lots of spare beds, they say—and they're not saying what for. That's why I got to find Mr Slaney. He's wanted over here sharp-like, and he's not in quarters. You've not seen him, eh?"

"Not yet. Corporal, hang on a moment. Tell me. Who's coming in? Our own wounded from France? Has there been a showdown?"

He said he couldn't say about that, he was sure. "But you take a tip from me, Miss Dillon, and nip down to the Pack Store smart and get all the stores you can out of Staff there. You'll be needing them, I reckon."

I put down the receiver and went back to the fire. The hearth was now very hot, yet I felt suddenly cold. I had a brother in the R.A.F. in France; another on a ship at sea. My elder brother, the sailor, had been at Narvik, and we had nursed men from that affair. The papers might call this a phoney war, but I knew, as did every other nurse in the hospital, that, phoney or not, already the young men had died.

Gabriel glanced at me curiously. "Would there be a wee flap on, Miss Dillon?"

"So Corporal Jenkins thinks." I told him about it as I ladled out the porridge. Mary came back when I was half-way through, so I had to start my story all over again.

Mary said she did not believe a word of it. When Gabriel vanished with a tray of porridge plates she added, "I'll bet it's only another exercise, Clare. You know how the G.O.C. adores exercises—and Jenkins adores spreading careless talk. I'll bet Joe Slaney's sound asleep in his bed at this minute and hasn't answered the 'phone because he hasn't heard it ring. That young man's far too lazy to dream of getting out of bed one minute before nine. If the day ever dawns when Joe Slaney appears to do a round before nine-thirty, then, and then only"—she picked up another loaded tray—"will I take this war seriously. Until then no one is going to persuade me that this is anything more than Jenkins' usual bout of alarm and despondency."

"And why," demanded a slow voice from behind us, "is Jenkins spreading alarm and despondency on this, a fine May

19

morning when the flowers are blooming, the birds are singing tra-la, and all the world's a song? Good morning, girls."

We did not need to turn round to recognize the owner of that drawling voice. Mary said simply, "My God. That does it." She handed her tray to Archibald, who had returned with the empty egg plate, and turned round. "Tell me, Mr Slaney, is Jerry with us? If not, what on earth are you doing up at this hour?"

Joe Slaney, the Ob. Block M.O., was a very tall, very thin young man, with shoulders so broad that until the theatre V.A.D.'s had assured us they remained broad in a cotton vest, we had all been convinced that his uniform jacket shoulders were grossly over-padded. He had very black hair, so black that it was faintly bluish, a long, thin, pale face, with a surprisingly strong jaw. Surprising, because Joe Slaney never gave the appearance of having strength in anything but the formation of his bony skeleton. His eyes were his best feature; they were well set, and a brilliant blue. He was about twenty-eight, but he still did not know what to do with his hands and feet, unless on a dance floor, where he turned into a professional. From what I had seen of him in the past few months he was far too good at dancing, and not much good at anything else; but, to be fair—and that was not easy, since I never cared for our M.O.—I had to admit to Mary that we had little opportunity of judging his knowledge of medicine, since he had so little opportunity for practising medicine in the Block. Normally he spent three-quarters of his working day in our hall drinking tea; the remaining quarter he devoted to filling in forms and chatting with the patients. Being an Irishman, he never stopped talking; his one great charm was his speaking voice, which was deep, as soft as Archibald's, and always slow, as if he had all eternity in which to complete a sentence.

He pushed his cap back on his head with a jerk of one thumb and smiled at Mary's astonishment. "All things are possible, Mrs Frantly-Gibbs. Jerry may be taking tea with the O.C. right now, for all I know. I know nothing. No one ever tells me anything. Some brutal character threw me out of my bed in short order fifteen minutes ago and told me to come over here—so here I am. The good God alone knows why. I've no conception." He drifted over to my side and peered into the empty tea bucket. "Would there be a drop of that left, Miss Dillon?"

"About half an inch of dregs. Cold, and near solid. Does it appeal to you?"

He leant against the wall, as if he was too weary to carry his own weight any longer. "Tea always appeals to me. And why wouldn't it, when I've had no breakfast? Would you have a spare mug there?"

I said, "I've got a message for you first. Jenkins rang for you just before you came in. He says there's some sort of a flap on, and you're wanted over there, sharp-like."

"There's always a flap on." He searched among the dirty crockery, and found a clean mug. "By the time I've got this tea hot there'll be a new flap, and Jenkins will be ringing round again." He emptied the tea bucket into a saucepan and thrust it on to the glowing coal. "You've a good fire here."

"It ought to be. I used half a tin of polish getting it going. Oh, lor'! That reminds me! Sister!"

"What about Sister?" He was absorbed with his tea-brewing. "Hasn't she turned up? Jenkins flapping for her too?"

I said, "She's on all right. Doing a round. I'd better fetch her."

He glanced at me. "Why? Think she'll be wanting some tea too?"

Mary guffawed over her table-clearing. "Not her, Mr Slaney! Miss Thanet's a keen type. She's had us both on the carpet already. She says she's going to run the Ob. Block like a proper hospital ward."

"Is she now?" His brewing was done, and he smiled at Mary as he sipped the nauseating liquid. "This I must see. Thanet now—wouldn't she be the new girl who arrived yesterday? Keen type, is she? Well, now, there's an exhausting prospect. And what did she beat you girls up about?"

Sister's return prevented our telling him. Although neither Mary nor I liked Joe Slaney, he was so much a part of the Ob. Block furniture that we had grown used to having him around, and regarded him as a necessary obstacle of our working lives, whom we had to walk round and feed with tea. Miss Thanet's expression when she joined us showed how much she disapproved of the V.A.D.'s treating M.O.'s as part of the furniture. She greeted Joe primly "Good morning, Mr Slaney."

He waved his mug at her. "Hallo, Sister. Would you care to join me in a cup?"

She smoothed her cuffs. "Not just now, thank you. Would you care to do your round?"

He closed his eyes. "It's not yet nine in the morning, and there's Jenkins beefing for me, and you, Sister, asking me to do a round. Now, will you be the ministering angel that you are—and not give me such shocks?"

Miss Thanet's mouth tightened in the manner that I had already come to recognize as a sign that someone was in for trouble. "I see. Since you are here, Mr Slaney, would you be good enough to give me some advice?"

Joe opened his eyes and smiled at her. Mary grinned at me—she was standing behind Sister, and could grin with impunity. "Sister," said Joe, "I never give advice. Not any more. The

21

Hippocratic spirit has long been beaten out of me, and with it has gone most of the medicine I once knew. I now content myself with giving out aspirins and iodine, and when I'm not dispensing the two I'm filling in forms. I know my place."

She looked as if she would like to hit him. "There is a man in Bed 18 I'm worried about. He's complaining of epigastric pain, and has a raised pulse-rate."

Joe bowed gallantly. "If you took his pulse, Sister, I'm not at all surprised to hear that it's racing. I don't doubt that most of the chaps in there have raised pulses and blood-pressures this morning."

She ignored his complaint magnificently. "I would like you to look at him, Mr Slaney."

He put down his mug reluctantly. "For you, Sister, I will do anything. But will you just tell me one thing? Would this ailing soldier by any chance be a fairish chap with the name of Marsden? A chap with a scar over his right eye-brow?"

"That's right." She looked surprised. "Do you know him? He said he only came in the night."

"Indeed I know him. Very well. He's working his way through Conybeare, is Marsden. I think he must have borrowed the book from somewhere; he always manages to have the classic symptoms. Last time he came in he had acute abdominal pain; the time before"—he grinned at her astonished face—"it was the shocking renal colic; before that—as I remember—his heart was going into failure—or it might have been then that he had the ugly gangrene of the left foot. It took your nurses here a lot of washing to get off the green dye. Poor Marsden; I've to hand it to him; he's putting in a lot of medical reading to get that ticket of his. Snag is he doesn't recollect that once, long, long, ago, we chaps read the books, too. Who let him in last night?"

She consulted the report-book. "The O.M.O. for the night. His initials are D.B.B."

Joe glanced at the book over her shoulder. "David Brown must be slipping. He does not generally fill us up with lead-swingers—but even Homer sometimes nods. Right, Sister. Let's go and look at his epigastrium. In one moment. First I suppose I had better let the miserable Jenkins know I'm here." He took up the telephone. "Jenkins? Slaney here. They say you've been ringing for me." He listened for a couple of seconds, then said calmly, "Now why could you not have said that to Miss Dillon in the first place? Right, man. I'll be across. I've to see a sick man first. I'll come when I'm done."

When we were alone Mary said, "I really thought she was going to throw something at him."

"Wouldn't have blamed her if she had." I swept out the hearth. "That man is the end."

22

She glanced up from the kitchen table she was scrubbing. "You loathe his guts, don't you, Clare?"

"Don't know about that. A person has to be definite for you to work up a good hate of him. You have to know someone to loathe them. I don't know Joe. The man's a walking bunch of poses; he's never natural for three minutes on end." I turned my broom upside down and pulled off a lump of fluff from the hairs. "I wish they'd either give us back our orderlies or let us have new brooms. I can't sweep anything with this monstrosity! It's worn to the wood, and makes dirt instead of removing it. Why can't the Army give us decent brooms?"

"Stop talking like Sister, dear," she said placidly. "You've done six months. Since when has the Army replaced any object before it falls into little pieces? That broom's got at least seven good hairs in it."

"That's true." I bent my back again. Then I had an idea. "Maybe, as Sister obviously intends to be a new broom sweeping clean, she might——"

"Clare." Mary's calm voice interrupted me. "I can stand a lot—but not you making horrible cracks. On with your sweeping, slave, and no more mutinous talk." But despite this admonition, she stopped scrubbing herself and tilted her head as if listening to something. "Stop banging that grate a second, Clare." She walked to the entrance door. "Come over here. Can you hear what I hear?"

I joined her, broom in hand. "That's a band. Jenkins was right. Some one is moving out."

She looked towards the ward entrance. "Sister's happy with Joe. Let's go up on the D.S. balcony and see if anything is in sight."

We ran up the iron staircase that connected our ramp with the Dirty Surgical Block above. The upper-storey blocks all possessed balconies which ran their full length and overlooked the square. The D.S. balcony had the advantage of being built parallel with the main hospital entrance, and from that balcony you could see over the flat arch to the road that lay beyond. When we reached the upper storey the road was occupied only by a line of stationary ambulances, but the sound of music drawing nearer acted as a Pied Piper to the staff, and the balcony round us filled rapidly with V.A.D.'s holding brooms and dusters, scarlet-caped Sisters with charts under their arms, M.O.'s in khaki, patients in blues, and a small group of overalled orderlies, who, seeing the M.O.'s stubbed their cigarettes and tucked them behind their ears.

Joe Slaney propelled an indignant Miss Thanet into the space by my elbow. She frowned at us. "I'm sure we should not have all left our Block."

"Relax, Sister," advised Joe. "The Ob. Block'll survive. The chaps we're about to see may not. This is a new experience for you. Make the most of it. You may not look on them again."

She frowned at him instead of Mary and me. "I don't understand you, Mr Slaney?"

"You will, when you've been here a while longer." He draped his angular body sideways against the balcony rail. "A band in this camp is synonymous with trouble. Trouble ahead, trouble past. They play merry little tunes when they march the boys back from a soldier's funeral. Courage music. They lay it on again when boosting the boys off. This is the works, you'll understand. Away with you, boys; fight for England, Home, and Glory, and shed your last drop of blood—to music."

She turned on him furiously. "What are you doing in that uniform if you feel like that."

He smiled at her as if she was a foolish child. "And did I say one word about how I feel? And have you not noticed this, Sister?" He touched the twined snake badge in his lapel. "Strictly non-com., that's Slaney. I'm just the chap that stands by with the needle and the thread to stitch up the pieces of the poor devils who get blown apart. I'm no man of action."

Her colour rose, making her look very attractive. "Then you've no business to scorn those who are willing to do the fighting for you."

"And when did I say I scorned them?" he drawled. "I've no scorn for anyone—not for the back-room boys, not even for the big-time politicians who shout and rant on about that fine last drop of blood. Not that there isn't one question I'd like to ask the big boys."

"Which is?" Her voice was razor-edged.

"Whose blood, chum?" murmured Joe Slaney. "Whose blood? Not your own; that's for sure. But hold it, Sister! Here they come."

The bandsmen, marching ahead, led the regiment that was marching in battle order down the road that ran past the hospital. The marching men whistled to the music; the soldiers on the balcony with us, and the sick soldiers in their beds on that flat arch of the hospital across the square, whistled with their colleagues. No woman watching whistled; we only stood very still—we were too far from the men on the road to need to force ourselves to smile. We had seen this scene re-enacted so many times in the last couple of weeks, when rumour after rumour had raced round the camp, and every rumour added to the dark score of something being very wrong in France. After each grim rumour another regiment was moved from the great camp around the hospital, marched in battle order down that white

24

road in the sunshine that was as constant as the music that always accompanied soldiers marching to battle.

Miss Thanet could not know what her fellow-women were thinking. She raised herself on her toes. "I think this is all rather thrilling."

I saw Mary look at Sister in silence. No one said a word. Mary's husband was a Regular soldier, a major in a Rifle Regiment. We were still silent when the marching men had vanished and the last faint notes of the music faded. I tucked my broom under my arm and followed Mary and Sister down the iron stairs. Just before I reached the bottom I stopped to pluck more fluff from my broom-head, and while doing this glanced up at the D.S. balcony, that had now emptied as quickly as it had filled. Only Joe Slaney remained on the rails. He was staring at the road, his hands threading and rethreading the rubber of his stethoscope through his fingers. He looked as if he were watching something important, and, wondering what there was to see, I went a few steps up again. The road was empty, but Joe did not look away, or notice what I was doing. His face wore an expression I had not seen on it before; he looked curiously vulnerable, and at the same time knowledgeable. He looked as if he were looking at the future. The future was something that none of us in that hospital ever talked about. We seldom talked about the past either. We who were young that summer had been born during, or in the shadow of, one war; a war our parents told us, that had been fought to end war; a war on whose ending —so our parents told us—every one suddenly burst out singing. As soon as we could read, or listen to broadcast news, we had realized that these tales our parents told us were fairy tales that belonged in the same category as Cinderella and Snow-white. We enjoyed the tales; we did not believe them; we had no reason to believe them, having grown only to exchange our school uniforms for other uniforms, to spend the high summer of our lives in another war; a war for which we could scarcely be held responsible, since most of us were too young to possess so much as a vote. We possessed only our youth; a slightly cynical tolerance of our elders and all authority; and a capacity for appearing bored. That last was our great secret defence.

I looked once more at Joe Slaney, and wondered why his defences were down. I could not guess the answer, so I tucked the broom under my arm once more and went back to my sweeping.

2

END OF THE BEGINNING

MISS THANET was unlucky. She spent most of her first two hours on duty in the Observation Block, drawing up work-lists and reorganizing what equipment we had; then a new order from the Company Office caused her to tear up her work-lists and to instruct Mary and me that the equipment was to remain where it was for the time being.

"Or the duration," murmured Mary, as she and I carried the kitchen table back to its former site beside the grate.

Sister looked at Joe who had returned to us, and was sitting at the table, drinking tea out of a cup this time. "Will you please tell me, Mr Slaney, just how do we empty the whole Block? What do we do with the men?"

Joe found a spot among the many papers on the desk for his saucerless cup, put it down lovingly, and picked up the typed order that had just come in. "We do just what it says here, Sister. We discharge all who are fit to be discharged, transfer those who are not."

"Transfer—to where? We can't send them to the other blocks, as this order applies to every block. And how can any of the men be fit for discharge if they've been admitted as needing hospital-ization?"

Joe read the order carefully. "With the exception of Marsden, I agree with you. Despite what the Company Office imagines, we don't admit at random, just because we consider the soldiery needs a rest. Just let me take all this in a moment, Sister; there's generally a loophole somewhere if you look hard enough. Hold it." He beamed at her. "Here we are. This lets us out. Here." He thrust the paper at her. "Read that last paragraph."

She read it aloud. " 'No patient may remain longer than twenty-four hours in the minor blocks such as Observation.' " She looked up. "That doesn't give us much help, surely?"

"Well, now, I'm not sure that it doesn't," said Joe, watching Mary and me. He nodded at us, as if to say he agreed that this was going to mean a damned awful lot of work for us, but there was no way round it. "This'll be the way of it, Sister. The chaps we can transfer we don't have to worry about. They'll not be transferred in this hospital, as you imagine, but go to some other place farther inland. All we've to do for them is see their notes are up to date, get their kit from the Pack Store, bung them on

26

stretchers or wheel-chairs, and leave the rest to the Office. On past showing a convoy'll take 'em off our hands around lunch-time. The chaps who are going to be our big problem are those who aren't ill enough to be transferred by Office standards, but aren't well enough by our standards to be bunged back to the camp. They are the chaps who will need the loophole, and this is what we'll do." He pulled the report-book from the litter of forms that buried it and opened it at the right place. "We'll discharge all the non-transfers this morning. We have to do that, as the book of words says so, but it does not say one word about admit-ting or readmitting. So we'll readmit the lot; minus Marsden. It'll mean a packet of work, and produce a mountain of forms, which will make the back-room boys in the Office as bucked as hell, and highly impressed with our zeal. Nothing pleases the back-room boys so much as the very devil of a lot of forms—and in triplicate! That really gets 'em hopping with joy, and why shouldn't we make them happy? There's no doubt at all that if we play our cards properly we may get ourselves promoted for this, Sister. So let's get cracking."

She looked quite dazed. "It seems such a waste of time?"

"And why worry about that? The time belongs to the Army. Hand me that file of discharge forms like a splendid girl, and I'll make out a list with this report-book. You can be filling in the forms with me. Then we can go and check up on the men, in case we have second thoughts about whom to transfer and whom to keep, and later come back and sign them."

"If you say so, Mr Slaney." Sister wore the pained air of a well-trained nurse who obeys a doctor—under silent protest. She turned to Mary. "Will you two V.A.D.'s carry on with your—er —usual routine for now?"

"I hope your V.A.D.'s are feeling strong, Sister," murmured Joe, scribbling a list of names, "as they've a packet of running back and forth with kit to do." He gave her the list. "Those are certain transfers. If you give them to your girls they can be getting on fetching that lot of kit while we work out the rest."

It was obvious that Sister had no idea what he was talking about, or what Mary and I were to do with the list. She had, however, a very good idea of how to cover ignorance with an efficient manner.

"Will you see to this, please, Mrs Frantly-Gibbs? Take Miss Dillon to help you, and report to me again when you have finished."

Mary and I went into the first ward. "Bless the girl," said Mary quietly, "she's clean out of her depth, and damned if she's going to let on. I'm beginning to agree with you, Clare. I think I'm going to like her." She raised her voice. "A word in your ears, gentlemen." She read out the names that applied to that ward.

27

"You're going to be transferred. Will you start packing, then get into bed, and let us have your blues so that we can get your uniforms?"

The up-patients crowded round us. "Do you know where we're going, Mrs Frantly-Gibbs?" asked Gabriel.

"No idea." She smiled at him. "Your guess is as good as mine. We just know you are going. Here." She gave him the list. "Go and tell these other transfers to get packing, will you, Gabriel? There'll be more to go after this, but we can get on with this lot. While you are doing this for me Miss Dillon and I can start shifting the sheets."

Fifteen minutes later we staggered across the square with the first load of soiled sheets, pillow-cases, shirts, and blues. When we reached the Pack Store we heaved our bundles on to the wooden counter, and were greeted by a resigned "Ob. Block emptying, ladies? Thought as much!" from the staff-sergeant in charge.

Staff-sergeant Williams was a Regular soldier in his late forties. He was a good staff-sergeant, moderately liked, so we were told, by the men, adored by the V.A.D. staff. He treated us all with paternal kindness and phenomenal patience, and had guided each of us in turn through the various stages of procedure and many complicated little forms that must be filled in before you can acquire so much as a pocket handkerchief for a sick soldier. His patience was second only to his omniscience about Army life, the affairs of the hospital, and happenings of the camp. Corporal Jenkins on the switchboard might occasionally hand on a false rumour; Staff Williams never gave gratuitous information about anything not directly concerning his Pack Store, but he always knew the answer to any question put to him. As Mary had told me to remain in the Store and check the first batch while she returned to the Block for more, I undid the knotted sheet of one bundle and asked, "What's this flap about, Staff? France?"

"That's right, miss. Let's have them shirts first." He licked his pencil and looked at me. "Them Frogs is the trouble. There's bad goings-on over there."

I arranged the shirts in a row. "What sort of goings-on?"

He pushed the stub of pencil behind one of his ears and sorted the remaining clothes neatly as he answered. "As I see it, miss, it's this way. Jerry—now, he's a fighter. The Froggie—he's what you can call a fighting-man, too, when he's got his heart in it. From what I hear from the lads as have come back on their leave or sick, this time Froggie, he just ain't got his heart in it. And they do say"—he glanced round with the instinctive caution of a Regular soldier; a caution that had nothing to do with any official enemy and careless talk, but was simply the result of the

28

many soldiering years in which he had learnt that it was a mistake ever to be seen casually chatting by a superior, even when his hands were at work, as they were now, folding soiled clothes. We were momentarily the only occupants of his store, so he went on, repeating himself—"they do say as this time the Froggie ain't got what you might call much discipline. Now, you got to hand it to Jerry, miss—Jerry's got discipline all right—same as our own lads. You tell Jerry to march; he marches. Our lads too. But Froggie, he always was a one to argy-bargy; remember the last little lot, I do, when I was a lad over there meself. From what they tells me"—he pushed the clothes aside and leant farther over the counter—"Froggie, he carries argy-bargy-ing something cruel right now, so that's why they got to pitch our lads over there fast like as they're doing now. Got to stop the argument some way, they have, so they're sending our lads in to break it up and hold Froggie back, like."

I said slowly, "Staff, are the French running away?"

He removed the stub of pencil from behind his ear and scratched the side of his nose with the blunt end. "I'm not over there, miss. I don't know no more than what you do what's going on, what with all I hear from the lads—and all that talk we hear on the wireless. Talk." He grimaced. "I dunno. Seems as that's all most of 'em can do. Talk." He shifted the final bundle of that first batch on to the floor on his side. "That the lot for now, miss? Want to take the stuff back with you?"

"Please." I pulled a collection of soldiers' receipts from my bib pocket. "I've got their forms." He wandered off to his shelves with the forms. When he returned with the khaki bundles I asked, "Staff, what do you think? This is just another flap, or the real thing?"

He smiled a little wearily. "I got twenty-four years' service, Miss Dillon. I don't think no longer." He leant on the counter again. "You don't want to let these things worry you, miss. All be the same in a hundred years' time."

I said, "I can't help worrying. That's why I want to know what's going on to-day. You're a Regular; you'll know the difference between an exercise and real trouble. Is this just another game to boost our morales?"

He glanced round, even more cautiously than last time. "You got someone over there, miss? Your boy friend?"

"No. One of my brothers. Twin brother."

"That's so?" His voice softened. "Young chap he'll be—begging your pardon, miss. Reckon you and he are pretty close?"

"Pretty close."

"What's his regiment?"

"No regiment. He's in the R.A.F.—a P.O. on Blenheims."

"He'll be a Regular?"

"Yes."

I waited. I knew I ought to be hurrying back to all the work there was to do in the Ob. Block, but I had to stay. I had been too occupied with my fire and Miss Thanet to pay much attention to this particular flap, until I saw that expression on Joe Slaney's face. I was not in the habit of setting any store on anything Joe Slaney did or said, but his expression had worried me, and I wanted the opinion of a wise old soldier like Staff Williams. I knew I could not hurry him into speech, that his answer was not going to help lessen the nagging worry for Charles I had had all morning; but I still wanted to hear what he had to say. In his own time he told me.

"Seems," admitted Staff Williams, "as this time it ain't no exercise, miss. Seems as there's a big do going on. Seems as they're expecting us to fill up sharp—with our own lads from the other side."

"Is there a big battle going on? At last? There was nothing on the News about it this morning."

"That's right, miss. There wasn't." He lowered his already quiet voice. "It's been going on some time, so they say. Our lads have been moving up Belgium way. They're still up there, some of 'em. And they do say as that Leopold's asking Jerry for his cards."

"Staff! He can't!" I watched his expression. "Or—has he done it already?"

"That's what they tell me, miss."

We looked at each other in silence. I did not ask who had told him all this; there are certain questions you do not ask soldiers. That fact does not stop their answers to other questions being frequently right.

"What about the French? They can't give up. And they needn't. They've got the Maginot."

He said laconically, "That's a fact, miss. Maybe it'll hold."

"You don't think it will? Isn't it meant to be—what's the word—impregnable?"

"So they says, miss. But I did hear as there's a gap there somewhere, and if I hears it you can lay to it, miss, Jerry, he's heard it too. If there's a way through Jerry'll find it. Sharp as a needle, Jerry is, and he knows how to fight." He looked at and through me. "I got my lad over there too. Fitter, he is—ground crew, R.A.F. It could be as he's in the same lot as your brother. I mind as he was fitting Blenheims last time he got his leaf. He"—a slow smile illuminated his stolid, pleasantly grim face—"got his tapes too, then, same as his dad. Doing all right, he is. Reckon you and me had best get out the flags, miss. Reckon your brother and my lad may be home a lot sooner than we thought." Another V.A.D. came into the store then; he

30

straightened his shoulders and became his official self. "Morning, Miss Carter. I been expecting you Acute Medical ladies! Over here with your lot, please, miss. Miss Dillon'll want to use her corner again with her next lot."

I waved a hand at him. "Thanks, Staff. See you later."

He gave me a little nod. "That's right, miss."

Agatha Carter heaved her bundle on to the counter. "Talk about a flap, Clare! We're shifting all our T.B.'s this morning. We'll have nothing left but gastrics this evening. How about you?"

"Far as I know, we're shifting the lot. But I bet we'll be full again this evening. The Ob. Block's always full."

Agatha said she wished she worked in the Ob. Block. "You girls may see the seamy side of life in the Army—but you do have a gay time."

I smiled. "Gay is the word, dear. We've got a new Sister, and she's got a fine new lamp. She's been rubbing it hard all morning. Came on an hour early to do the job properly."

"How perfectly ghastly!" Agatha changed her mind about working in the Ob. Block. "I prefer our old war-horse in A.M. She may be hell, but at least she never bothers us provided we leave her alone to her beloved M.O.'s."

Staff Williams coughed discreetly. "Ready if you are, Miss Carter?"

Agatha beamed at him. She was an apparently ordinary-looking young woman with very fair hair and very good teeth. Whenever she smiled she seemed to show too many teeth, good as they were, but, since she had a great deal of sex appeal, her teeth did not matter. "It's all yours, Staff!" she announced.

I watched Staff Williams' expression alter slightly as he sorted her bundle, then went back across the square. I had a lot to think about, but for a few moments I stopped worrying if this flap was going to affect Charles, and thought about Agatha. Not even the fatherly Staff Williams was paternal when Agatha was about; I wondered casually about that quality which she possessed and I did not, and what the possession must feel like. The fact that I lacked her appeal did not bother me, because it was clean out of my hands, and I have never been a person to bother much about things that are beyond me. But it interested me, and I was still brooding over Agatha, Helen of Troy, and Miss Betty Grable when I met Mary in the middle of the square.

"There's all hell going on in the duty-room now," she told me cheerfully. "The C.O. and Major Endsby are both there putting their heads together with Sister about the empty beds we haven't got. Sister looks ready to go up the wall. That first list of discharges has been scrapped."

"What does Joe say to that?"

"I left him making more tea. He's too busy to bother with anything else. Oh, yes—the post has come. I've got yours in my bib." She thrust her bosom at me. "Help yourself. I haven't a hand."

I pulled five letters from her apron bib. Three were hers from her husband. One was my mother, the other from Charles. The sight of his handwriting made me feel much more cheerful. "If the mail is still coming it can only be a flap. Staff and Jenkins must be wrong."

"Well, dear," she said, "they are pets, but they are old soldiers, and they have to spin us horror-stories. It's all part of the game."

I read my letters rapidly as I walked more slowly the remaining distance to the Ob. Block. Just as I arrived Joe was ushering the C.O. and his attendant major from the door. He waited for me to precede him into the Block again. "Brother Charles flourishing?"

I looked up at him. "How in the world did you know I had a brother called Charles? I never told you?"

"No one ever tells me anything. But I keep my ear to the ground—and have no shame when it comes to eavesdropping. How's big brother Luke getting on at sea?"

I smiled at him. Charles' letter had been pleasantly normal; my mother's had contained the splendid news that Luke was in hospital in Scotland with a broken leg that was doing well, and was going to keep him on land and out of the War for at least two months, according to my father, a general practitioner. I felt much happier. The sun was shining, and the world was fun, even if it did go in for major or minor wars and flaps. "Brother Luke's doing nicely. He's busted his right tibia playing hockey and is in a nice safe hospital bed. Thank you very much, Mr Slaney. Anything else you'd like to know about my family?"

"Just one thing. How in the name of God, will you tell me, did your brother break his tibia playing hockey?"

"I've no idea. Mother doesn't say. Maybe the Navy version of hockey is a rough game."

He said if there was one thing he detested above all else in life it was playing rough games. "Don't you agree, Sister?"

Miss Thanet was too occupied with paper-work to pay attention to him. She gave me another list. "These are the last transfers. They must be ready to move out at eleven-thirty. When you've got their kit organized will you go to the Orthopædic Block and collect all their X-rays and notes?"

For the rest of that day, and the remainder of that week, we Ob. Block V.A.D.'s traipsed backward and forward across the square, exchanging khaki for blues, blues for khaki. Sister and Joe Slaney sat side by side at the desk table; with each passing day they came closer to being totally buried beneath the mountain of forms on that desk. The camp rumours increased as fast as did the forms; every day another regiment marched to music along the road in front of the hospital, and we grew so used to the sound of a band that we stopped bothering to go up to the D.S. balcony to watch the men go by.

By Saturday evening our feet were exhausted, our spirits decidedly low. Even the calm Mary said she felt jittery. "Have you got a date to-night, Clare? If not come with Mick and me to the theatre. The show'll be very blue, but it'll be something to do. Mick'll love to produce another man. The poor boys are just as worn out as we are with all these tedious exercises."

Mick Hammond was Mary's cousin. He was a captain in the Gunners, and very useful to Mary whenever she needed an escort in her husband's absence, as Mick appeared to be a permanent fixture in the camp. Men might come and go, but Mick Hammond remained, much to his annoyance, as his own company had moved out weeks ago. I had nothing better to do, so I agreed with thanks. Mary rang Mick at the last moment, but there were so many surplus young men in the camp that that made little difference to Mick's providing another man to round off our party. He offered Mary a selection of five names; she chose one, Bill Something. "He's a harmless soul, Clare, and you'll have to like him, as he hasn't enough character—or chin—to be disliked."

Bill Something also possessed an aged Bentley, so we drove to the Garrison Theatre. The variety show was very bad, but the troops sat through it with admirable phlegm; the jokes were filthy, and only very rarely funny as well. Mick and the chinless Bill grew more and more uncomfortable at each joke. Mary soothed them, "You don't have to worry about me, my dears, I being an old married woman—and as for young Clare, she's still at the stage of innocence where such muck goes clean over her head." To prove this she demanded, "Did you follow that last one about a man's bicycle?"

I leant forward in my seat to answer. "No. I was just going to ask one of you to explain."

Mick Hammond let out a shout of laughter; Bill turned pink; Mary said gently, "No dear. Don't ask that, because none of us will." She looked at the two men. "Relax. See what I mean?"

The show was stopped by the theatre manager just before the interval. "Ladies and gentlemen, I have an announcement to make." He waited for the delighted roar that followed his words; the troops always roared that way when addressed as gentlemen, because, we guessed, they felt the roar was expected. Troops are obliging men, and invariably react as expected. The

33

manager went on to request all officers to return to their Messes immediately. This request was greeted with a far more genuine roar: "Who'd be a something officer?"

Our escorts were not distressed by the recall in itself; these recalls were very frequent, and after being hauled back to their Messes they were seldom kept for more than a couple of hours, but they were distressed at the thought of having to leave Mary and me to make our own way home. "Sure you girls don't mind walking back through the camp? Sure you wouldn't like to ride some of the way with us?"

Mary sent them off on their own. "Clare and I'll be all right. We aren't frightened of soldiers—and we're nurses. You may not know it, but our uniform is the finest armour a girl can have. No one makes an improper pass at a V.A.D. Get going, boys, or you'll catch it from your boss."

Mary was quite right. We sat through the rest of that dreadful show, simply because we were glad to sit down. Later we walked slowly back to our Mess through the heart of the camp in which—according to rumour—there were still around one hundred thousand men. It was evening, and growing dusk, but not one soldier did more than whistle, or sing a snatch of "Nursie, come over here, and hold my hand," or tell us brokenly that we were the reason they had left home. As Mary said, the only thing that would have worried us would have been if we had failed to raise a cat-call or wolf-whistle. "When that happens, Clare, then a girl knows she's past the girl stage, and all that's left to her is to grow old gracefully."

Next morning Mary and I again had the same off-duty, this time from ten until one, so we decided to go together to the garrison church. We went there straight from the Block, wearing our indoor uniform and scarlet-lined blue cloaks.

The church was almost full when we got there. As Mary led the way to the V.A.D.'s pew our aprons rustled, and on both sides of the aisle the men's heads swayed like twin fields of stubble corn in our direction. I noticed Joe Slaney's back in the R.A.M.C. officers' pew ahead of us. He was wearing his best uniform that morning; it was well-tailored, and his leather belt made his normally slim waist look in danger of breaking in two. Mary, noticing him too, whispered, "If that man gets much thinner he'll fade away. He's nothing but bone—not even skin."

The service was short, with plenty of hymns. The men's voices sounded tragically sincere and sad, as men's voices singing in chorus always do, if they are only singing *Sweet Violets*. One of the hymns we sang was *O God, our help in ages past.* That hymn reminded me suddenly of my father; it was his favourite hymn. I felt a queer little wave of homesickness,

34

hearing it that morning. I had never really missed my home or parents; I had loved both, but was much enjoying the glorious freedom of being on my own, and I liked my new job. But I can only hear music with my emotions; I cannot listen to it mathematically, as I believe a true musician can. That particular hymn, my father, and my childhood were all bound up together in a pleasantly vague yet satisfying memory. I thought about my father, and was glad that he was too old to fight in this war, and too busy with his practice at home to have time to know the War was on. The behaviour of the troops around me drew my attention back to the present. They were behaving very badly; their concentrated boot-scraping, cap-dropping, and yawns were infuriating their N.C.O.'s and enchanting Mary and me. She nudged me slightly. "Look at that sergeant on your right, Clare. He looks about to explode."

When the next week began properly the "Patients to remain in the Observation Block for twenty-four hours only" order was still in operation. Miss Thanet looked a little pale, but was otherwise composed; Joe Slaney produced a pound of tea for us. "I thought maybe your girls might be getting a little short of the stuff, Sister. My granny sent it me. Now we can really go to town and have a decent cup."

Mary, staggering under another bundle of kit, asked, "I suppose your granny didn't send you any poteen, Mr Slaney? That I could use."

Sister looked shocked; Joe unmoved. "Well, now, she didn't. But I'll write and ask for some, Mrs Frantly-Gibbs."

In the Pack Store even Staff Williams was wilting visibly; his assistants were near breaking-point. "For Gawd's sake, Miss Dillon! Not another pack from the Ob. Block! Give us a chance, miss! We won't have a spare set of blues left at this rate! O.K., miss! Hand it over."

Miss Thanet settled in admirably. She stopped calling us 'Nurse'; gave up her attempts to turn us into well-trained probationers; left us to get on with our own work, turning a blind eye to floor-polish as a fire-lighter, and to Mary's habit of serving meals with her sleeves rolled up—Mary wore the older version of the British Red Cross uniform, with long sleeves, and that habit had tried Miss Thanet sorely on her first day. Sister was also icily patient with our lethargic M.O., who alone remained unhurried during those hurried days, and obviously irritated her by his endless consumption of tea.

One Wednesday evening in that second week he stopped his car to offer me a lift home. "What's happened to your bike?" he asked, opening the door.

"Two flats. Fore and aft. I can't ride it."

"One doesn't bother you?"

I sat down in his little car, grateful of the opportunity to get off my feet. "Not really. It only means you bump a bit."

"You also ruin the wheels."

I said I did not hold with that theory. "I've proved it false. Not only me; every V.A.D. in the hospital rides on flats, and our wheels don't buckle."

"Why not be a real devil and mend the punctures? Or get the chaps to do it for you?"

"If you—or the O.C.——" I retorted bitterly, "would only leave us one able-bodied man in the Ob. Block for more than a few hours I could have my bike mended easily. As it is, the poor men have barely time to walk into the wards before we have to wrest their khaki off their backs; then no sooner have they climbed into bed to be examined than they are climbing out of bed into blues; then we are seizing their blues from them, and pitching them back into bed again to wait for their khaki. I wouldn't mind at all having someone mend my bike in his underwear, but soldiers are so frightfully proper. They'd be shocked to death if I wheeled my bike into the ablutions and asked them to fix it in their smalls." I had an idea, and looked at him hopefully. "I suppose you don't know anything about mending bikes?"

He smiled at the road ahead. "Not I. Not one thing. It devastates me to say so, you'll understand, Miss Dillon. There's nothing I'd like so much as to mend your bike—it's too bad that I can't do it for you. Machinery"—he almost sang the word, so slowly was he talking—"the internal combustion engine, the whole box of tricks, scare the daylights out of me. I wouldn't know where to start with any of them. I prefer sex as a hobby."

I said, "Is it the only alternative?"

He glanced at me. "Can you tell me a better?"

"I would have said yours was drinking tea."

"That's no hobby, woman," he replied mildly, "that's my virtue. Think of the good it does my kidneys."

I was not interested in his kidneys; there was something else I wanted to ask him. Since Miss Thanet's arrival he had not been free to natter with us as in the past, when Mrs Smith ran the Ob. Block. This was not only because of the increased rush of work, but because Miss Thanet clearly disapproved of our previous informality with our M.O., and was not disposed to turn a blind eye to this, as to so much else. Consequently Mary, Janice, and myself now avoided the duty-room as much as possible, and although this saved me a considerable amount of irritation—since sooner or later Joe Slaney invariably irritated me—I found it did shut down one of my most useful lines of information. Staff Williams could tell me a lot about the situation; but it was Joe Slaney who in the past had regaled Mary and me with the fascinating details of exactly what the O.C. said to

Major Endsby during that row in the R.A.M.C. Officers' Mess, and why Matron was insisting that Sister So-and-so should be sent to the Families Hospital as extra Sister, when the theatre was running short-staffed.

"Why did Mrs Smith move so suddenly, Mr Slaney? We thought she was with us for the duration."

"I hoped that, too," he agreed. "Strangely, she went only because she was posted. I gather Matron was as sorry to see her go as we were—and I know the O.C. liked her. She was a good soul, was old Mother Smith. She'd the right touch. But they are opening Clearing Stations all over the place. Hospitals, too."

"Where are they getting the staffs from? You can't produce trained nurses out of a bottomless hat."

"The big general hospitals are coping. All the Big Five, and the others. They're lending their nurses and medical staff to set up places like Garden East—that's the place all our chaps are going to from here. It's around sixty miles inland; an ex-looney-bin that's got two thousand Service beds to date." His dark face was illuminated by one of his rare genuine smiles. "The chaps'll like the difference."

"What difference?"

"Between a military and civilian hospital. In a civilian hospital a patient is a guest and not a convict."

I would have liked to disagree with him. I could not, as I knew nothing at all about civilian hospitals—fifty hours does not grant you any knowledge—and I knew that he was right about the Army. "Why did you become a soldier? Doctors can still be reserved, can't they?"

He said he had not the faintest idea.

"You must have volunteered, then?"

A corner of his mouth lifted. "Naturally. I'm the hero calibre. Don't I look it?"

"No."

He laughed. "Well, now, and to think that I walked into that —and with my chin. And since we're having such a fine time being frank with each other, there's a question I'd like to ask you, Miss Dillon. How old are you? Did you have to give a false age to get in?"

"No. I'm twenty."

"Are you now?" He ignored the road, and surveyed me coolly. "It's those big eyes of yours that fool one—and that schoolgirl haircut. Why do you wear your hair in that straight cut? Have you not heard of permanent waves, or do you not approve of them? Not, I'll grant you, that it doesn't suit you. It does. But it makes you rather unique in this era of curls, and that puzzles me. Why should you care to look unique?"

I said between my teeth, "Why shouldn't I?"

He concentrated on the road again. "It doesn't go with the rest of you. You're so very typical of the long-legged hand-me-my-hockey-stick-and-let's-have-a-damned-good-game English-woman, who's got a beautiful figure and does her damnedest to hide it. And it doesn't go with your leaping into the first available uniform and racing round with a broom and dustpan mentality. Those are both traditional and correct attitudes; your hair-style quarrels with them. It almost leads one to suppose the shocking heresy that maybe you've a mind of your own."

I said evenly, "If I owe this to two flat tyres, next time I'll walk."

"You can walk now if you wish. But as we're nearly at your Mess you might as well sit it out."

I turned on him. "Just what do you think I should be doing? Sitting by the burning home fires knitting? Entertaining the troops to coffee and macaroons?"

"Tea," he murmured dreamily, "with tea. Only the upper classes care for coffee, but the poor damned bastards of soldiers are too polite to say so. If you entertained them to tea and ham rolls you might be doing some good." He slowed to a stop by the side of the road to allow a small convoy of carriers to rattle by. "I imagine you feel bucked as hell that you're Doing Your Bit?"

"I wouldn't know." I watched the convoy. "No one tells me anything."

He took his hands off the wheel. "Suppose I tell you something?"

"Go ahead."

He smiled faintly as if I had made a weak joke. "Right. I'll do that. Why waste your time in this racket? If you want to nurse why not learn to do the job properly?"

"Someone has to be a V.A.D."

"Certainly they do. Sensible young women like your pal Mary Frantly-Gibbs, who've husbands and homes to return to when the party's over, and others, older than she, who can do a good job at it, as it's too late for them to do anything else. But a young, strong, damned healthy young woman like yourself has no business to stay here playing at the job. Unless," he added softly, "you are of the mind that this is just a game for the girls after finishing school. If it is I'd say you won't have much difficulty in graduating. Not with your legs."

"Graduating?"

"Getting a husband. Isn't that the main object of being finished? You come out, in a fine white dress, go to the right parties—and that just now means wearing a red cross on your bosom—and then sling your hooks."

His conversation had been only annoying me until now. I was

38

downright angry as I answered, "Mr Slaney, you offered me a lift home. Thank you very much. Had I realized what I was in for I would not have accepted your offer. Do you realize that you're being exceedingly rude?"

"So what? I've no nice feelings, and neither the pretensions nor desire to act like a little gentleman. I'm not often curious, but when I am I ask questions. I'll admit I'm curious about you, Miss Dillon, and if you don't want men to be curious about you" —he looked down at my ankles—"you ought to wear black woollen stockings and keep your dress-hems down to the ground. Legs like yours—in black silk—invite questions." He looked up at my face. "Or wouldn't you know about that."

"I know," I said—wearily, because I really was tired after all the running across the square I had done that day, "I know. I've two brothers, and one of them's my twin."

"So they've told you the facts of life? I wouldn't have thought it after watching your modest violet act in the hospital. Eyes to the ground when an M.O. comes in."

"That's because I like a quiet life." I met his eyes deliberately. "The way for a quiet life if you are a V.A.D. is to keep your eyes on the ground, and leave the M.O.'s to the Q.A.'s. And from what I've seen of M.O.'s, the ground is far more attractive."

He grinned. "Well, well, well. And there was I thinking you too much of a little lady ever to hit back." He started the car as the convoy had passed. "This is going to be interesting."

"What is?"

He said he would tell me some other time. "Over the dinner table, maybe. If you'd care to dine with me? Have to be in our Mess, I'm afraid, as we're all confined to camp, but the food's not bad. What about to-night, as we are both off?"

If we had not had the previous conversation I should have made a civil excuse about having a headache. I said, "Not to-night, thank you."

"Got a date?"

"No."

"Good God, woman! Then why not?" And he seemed honestly surprised.

"I don't like young doctors. I see enough of them at work."

"You're telling me you don't like doctors?" The car swerved dangerously and took his astonished attention from me. "My dear girl, you're talking absolute nonsense! Everyone likes doctors. We're highly respected citizens, our intentions are always honourable—they have to be, as we daren't risk breach of promise cases for fear of being struck off—and just think of the glamour attached to a medical man!"

"I don't care for glamour in men. And I didn't say I disliked all doctors, merely young doctors. At the smug stage. I like

39

doctors over forty-five—very much. My father's one, and so are his partners. I like them. They're kind—and polite."

He winced extravagantly. "Watch out. There go my back teeth. You shouldn't kick a man when he's driving, Clare. And don't tell me I've no right to call you Clare, because you've just given me the right by joining in a free for all. Not that I bear you any hard feelings about it. Just call me Joe next time you insult me." He swung into the drive that led up to the V.A.D.'s Mess. "You've given me quite a character, you know. I'm smug, unkind, impolite, glamorous. That's some list."

"You can omit the last one." I jumped out of the car and slammed the door. Our Commandant was standing within earshot on the top step by the front door, so I had to thank him more civilly than I would otherwise have done. "Thanks for the lift, Mr Slaney."

His vivid blue eyes were alight with laughter. He saluted Miss Moreby-Aspin, "Good evening to you, ma'am," then lowered his voice to me. "It's too bad you won't dine with me, Clare Dillon. I'd have enjoyed blacking the other eye—and you could have pushed my front teeth down after the back. Have a jolly evening with the girls. See you around the Block—if you ever look up from the ground. Good night."

Miss Moreby-Aspin called to me directly he drove away. "Dillon, m'dear, you're showing far too much hair under your cap. Pull it forward, girl! And what are you wearing on your legs? Black silk stockings? Go in and change them at once for your regulation grey wool!!"

Joe Slaney's attack had surprised me; Miss Moreby-Aspin's did not surprise me at all. And I knew quite well how to deal with her, and that was in the way that all women deal with their female officers after a few weeks' experience.

I said, "Yes, Madam; of course, Madam; I am so sorry, Madam. I'll change my stockings as soon as my grey wool are dry." I tugged my cap forward obediently and went inside with not the slightest intention of changing my stockings. Directly I was out of her sight I pushed my cap back on my head again.

It was a lovely evening and I had been looking forward to it all day, since free evenings were scarce in the Ob. Block. In a perverse fashion, now that I had refused Joe's unexpected invitation to dinner, the long, double-summertime hours of daylight that stretched ahead seemed empty. I had a bath, changed into a clean uniform dress, then wandered rather aimlessly round my bed, tidying the minute area that belonged to me in the converted drawing-room that I shared as a bedroom with nineteen other young women.

The room was large, well-proportioned, it had a high ceiling ornamented with gold leaf, three fine glass chandeliers that hung at intervals down the centre of the room, and four wide, long mirrors that were fixed to three of the walls, and were a veritable godsend now that it was a bedroom. The twenty Army beds were arranged at right angles to the walls, and down and across the centre of the room. My bed was one of those in the centre. The beds were identical, as were the twenty orange-boxes that served us as dressing-tables, lockers, and chests-of drawers combined. An immense variety of suitcases were piled under every single bed, the orange-boxes were littered with framed photographs of young men in uniform, and there were enough cosmetic-jars and bottles visible on every convenient and inconvenient ledge to stock a fair-sized beauty parlour. The drawing-room was called "The Jungle" by all but its occupants; we liked our bedroom. We liked the privacy that you can only acquire of necessity when living in a crowd; we liked the fact that, as there were so many of us in that room, at least one person's portable wireless was certain to be working; we liked our Commandant's theory that only the youngest V.A.D.'s should be subjected to living in a herd, which meant that the older, and more sedate members of our company were not there to see what time we came in at night, or complain because we fell asleep smoking in bed! above all, we liked the french windows that opened on to the garden, giving us the quickest route to the new bathrooms that had been built in the old conservatory, and the easiest route in and out of the Mess at any hour of the day or night, making it impossible for Madam to supervise our coming and going adequately. Miss Moreby-Aspin was a good soul who took her duties seriously; she even went round all the bedrooms at night, reading a roll-call before locking the front door. The way round her roll-call was simple; we used to make a point of returning from our dates at ten-thirty when she read the roll; obediently chanting, "Here, Madam," then smugly we donned our dressing-gowns over whatever we were wearing, seized our sponge bags, wandered out of the window to the conservatory for our baths, deposited our dressing-gowns and sponge bags in one of the bathrooms, and returned to our various escorts, who were waiting in their cars with the lights prudently switched off for us to continue our evening's entertainment.

The french windows were wide open that evening, but the room seemed airless. I blew some dust off Charles' photograph; wiped Luke's with an old apron, as Mary had spilt her tea over my orange-box that morning, then, feeling I had done enough cleaning for one day, took the assortment of daily papers I had brought from the sitting-room, some cigarettes, matches, and a rug and strolled out of the nearest window into the garden.

There were three tennis-courts laid out beyond the small,

sloping lawn outside our room. The first tennis-court was occupied by four V.A.D. cooks. "Want to cut in, Dillon?" they called amicably.

"No, thanks. My feet won't stand it. I'll watch." I spread out my rug and settled down on the lawn to read the newspapers. I did not spend long on them. Their news was old to the camp. I looked at Jane in the *Mirror*, because the boys were so fond of her. Charles said they never considered the day had begun on his station unless Jane had her clothes off at breakfast.

I pushed aside the paper, lay on my stomach in a position where I could watch the cooks idly. I found their tennis soothing to listen to as well as to watch. They played well together, and as my head twisted from side to side watching the ball I thought about Joe Slaney. I had been very cross with him in the car; I have a quick temper and like most quick-tempered people I get cross very easily, but find it hard to stay cross. I wondered why he had bothered to rouse me as he had; he reminded me, now I came to think of it, of the many young men my brothers had brought home—young men who attacked with yawns, belittled and scorned every serious subject of conversation, and infuriated my father and his friends. I smiled at the tennis-players, thinking how my father would describe Joe. "The worst type of medical man. He probably subscribes to one of these lily-livered peace unions!" I decided it was highly possible that Joe Slaney had belonged to the Peace Pledge Union, if the P.P.U. served tea at its meetings. His belonging to that would not have prevented his volunteering now. I knew that, because I had listened to and talked with those other young men when my father was out of the room. They talked differently in his absence—not because they were afraid of him, but because they were too polite to state their *real* feelings before him. The majority, like my brothers and myself, had long ago had their manners instilled by their nannies, and you cannot shed easily the teachings of an English nanny. It was our Nanny Haskins who was principally responsible for my thanking Joe for his lift. "Say thank you, dear, nicely. Look the lady or gentleman straight in the face. That's right, dear. Remember, never forget your manners."

Nanny Haskins had been very upset about Charles' flying. "Now, if it had been you, Miss Clare"—she had added the prefix when I left school—"I shouldn't have been surprised. You and Mr Luke were always a proper pair of tomboys! But Mr Charles was always the gentle one—like madam—with his playing the piano and writing stories. I always said you should have been the boy and he the girl—but there it is! And you're going to be a nurse? Whatever will you be up to next? You will mind

42

how you behave, Miss Clare—and be sure always to wear your vest. There's nothing like wool next to the skin—and I'm sure the Doctor will agree!"

Nanny Haskins was now retired. She was an old lady, but her strong sense of duty, her certainty of her correct place in society, and her fixation about vests were undaunted. A Conservative government, good digestion, and wool next to the skin, according to Nanny Haskins, solved most of life's little problems.

A small yellow Tiger Moth chugged its way over the sky like a fat homing bee. I rolled over to watch the moth until it disappeared in the direction of the Flying Training School at Upper Weigh, fifteen miles to the west, and wondered if Charles was flying to-day. I hated the thought of him flying as much as my mother did, but for his sake I was glad he had taken my father's advice and gone to Cranwell, as until he flew Charles had never been wholly alive.

He wrote me one letter when he first started flying: "Clare, you cannot know what beauty is until you get above the clouds. It's like being in a dream and not having to wake up, as the dream is all around you and belongs to you alone. I wish you could see it."

I could not see his dream, yet I could see Charles. Nanny was right; I might be Charles' twin, but I looked and thought like Luke. Possibly because we were so alike, Luke and I had always fought as small children; then later, when Luke vanished to Dartmouth, Charles and I grew up alone, and he and I had never had more than a mild argument in all our lives. Father said that was because Charles was like Mother and I was like him. He was probably right about that; my father was right about most things. He was one of the wisest men I ever met, and yet, returning to my original thoughts of Joe Slaney, I could not help wondering if Father had been right in his condemnation of those young men who filled our house at the week-ends.

I stared at the empty sky, trying to remember where they all were; David and Henry—they had been in O.U.A.S. at Oxford and were at some Flying Training School—or they had left it by now? Peter Billings had had one pip when I was last home; Peter Ash was an Ordinary Seaman—but what had happened to Michael Ash?

"Dillon! Wake up!" The shouts from the cooks interrupted my meandering thoughts on one Michael Ash. "Come over here and see what's coming in—come over here—by the road!"

I blinked and sat up. The cooks had left the tennis-court and were standing by the low hedge at the far side of the garden. There had once been a high, pointed iron railing separating that

43

hedge from the road; the railing had gone during my first month in the camp.

"What's the matter?" I stood up before I noticed the convoy of lorries that was coming towards us from over the hill. The hill was a long way off, and I had joined the others before the first lorry of that convoy reached us. "What's so special about this lot, girls?" I asked, feeling faintly annoyed at being hauled from my rug to watch what was a daily occurrence in the camp.

"You look," said one cook, "and see if you notice what we did. Seven lorries have been by already. This is the next batch."

I looked obediently at the lorries as they drove by; as I looked slowly I had the sensation that I was looking at one of those puzzle pictures you find in children's books. In those pictures you have to spot the objects drawn out of place.

I said, "What's the Army doing driving the R.A.F.? Why not R.A.F. drivers? R.A.F. lorries?"

They said the other lorries had been Army lorries too. "But they were full of R.A.F. And silent. As these are."

That, I realized then, was what was so strange. The backs of those lorries were open, and we could see they were packed with men. The men watched us as they passed by, and not one man made a sound. There were no catcalls or wolf-whistles; no shouts or snatches of song; only men watching us in silence.

I was noticing other things. "They're filthy. Look at their uniforms. But they can't be wounded. Those aren't ambulances."

The five of us sat down on the bank beside the road in the soft evening sunshine and stared at the men who stared so blankly at us. Some of the men stood, some sat, all were huddled in some enveloping garment—R.A.F. greatcoats, Army greatcoats, red hospital blankets; a few clutched the multicoloured knitted shawls the Red Cross provided, and hunched their shoulders like tired old women. The sunshine touched the colours with light, making them seem indecently bright in contrast to the grey, unshaven faces of the men.

Another cook said, "They look—frightened."

The girl who had spoken first disagreed, "Not so much frightened as old. They look terribly old," and none of us said any more.

That second convoy was followed by a third, then a fourth, each longer than the original seven lorries. At intervals three more convoys rolled by. We sat there for close on an hour, watching the dust rise from the road as the lorries, heavy with their silent cargoes, thundered on into the camp. When at last the road remained empty for several minutes we looked expectantly at the hill far on our right. There was no movement on that hill now, and the light summer dust was settling on the road again. The sun was still fairly high, yet I found I shivered, as if the evening had turned cold. Slowly, without speaking, we got up and walked back towards the house. Two of the cooks wandered off to the court they had just used, collected the balls, and lowered the net, although the evening was still perfect for playing tennis.

3

THE MEN COME HOME

I COLLECTED my rug and papers and went back to the "Drawing-room" without knowing why. I sat on my bed, lit a cigarette, then stubbed it out almost at once, the tobacco tasted sour. I walked restlessly over to one of the french windows and stood there staring at the still empty road. I was standing there a few minutes later when our Commandant came in: "Busy, Dillon?"

I turned. "No, Madam."

She came briskly into the room. "Just standing and staring, eh, m'dear?" And, since she always had a magnificent stock of platitudes handy, she added that the Devil could always find work for idle hands, so she had best give me a job to do!

We were all fond of our Commandant. Miss Moreby-Aspin was a kind, quite sexless person, who we felt would be insulted to be termed a woman. She clearly loved the War, and the opportunity it had given her to get back into uniform and assume her First War medal ribbons. We had never been able to discover if she had ever done any actual nursing, but she had an imposing number of years' service in the Red Cross to her credit, was a good administrator and caterer, and generally considered quite harmless. Her brisk bark and her platitudes she assumed with her uniform. In a dressing-gown she had sloping shoulders and a soft, cultured voice. We never saw her in mufti, and it was rumoured that she had never worn mufti, but had spent the period between the wars on the shelf of some large cupboard in the War Office labelled: Ladies Only Reserved For Emergency.

I asked if there was something I could do for her?

She slapped my back and said she could see the War really was making a man of me. "Afraid you were a bit too young and airy-fairy for the work when you first arrived, Dillon, m'dear! You looked as if the first puff of wind would bowl you over, with that match-stick figure of yours! Should have remembered you were a sailor's daughter. Nothing like a sailor for raising the Right Sort!"

Normally I enjoyed swopping platitudes with Madam, and much appreciated the fact that she ignored the years that had passed since my father left the Royal Navy and took up medicine. That evening I only smiled feebly, and reminded her that I was now a G.P.'s daughter.

She slapped me again. "Shows your father's made of the Right Stuff, Dillon. Now, m'dear, will you just run back to the hospital for me? I've left my glasses in Matron's office, and can't go meself as I'm tied to the 'phone. Polly's off this evening."

Polly was Miss Polinson, the Home V.A.D.

"Of course I'll go for them, Madam." I remembered my flat tyres. "Are you in a hurry, as I'm afraid I'll have to walk?" I explained why.

She was in a good mood, so she only repeated "For Want of a Nail" in full and told me to bustle to. "Take mine, Dillon. No punctures, mind!"

I was pleased with the excuse to go back to the hospital. I seized my black summer uniform straw hat, sat it on the back of my head, and cycled as quickly as I could back to the camp. I saw no sign of any of the lorries en route; when I had collected Madam's glasses I called in at the Ob. Block. Removals were going on there as usual, but neither Sister nor Mary had heard anything about my lorries. I walked over to Casualty and spoke to the Orderly M.O. and the Casualty V.A.D.; they knew nothing, but like Mary and Miss Thanet were eager to hear all I could tell them. After Casualty I went to the Pack Store— Staff Williams was missing; his corporal looked glum. "Coming in, did you say, miss. Thought as much. What's that? No, nothing at all in here. Can't be no wounded among 'em."

Feeling very dispirited, I cycled quickly and illegally across the square. No one stopped me until I sailed under the arch and ran into Joe Slaney. I ran into him literally, and had to jump off as I discovered belatedly that Madam's brakes did not work. "Sorry, Mr Slaney. Did I hurt you?"

He dusted his knees. "Not so you'd notice it." He looked at the cycle I had now retrieved. "I thought you had two flats, not no brakes?"

"This belongs to Madam." I explained what I was doing. "I thought you had the evening off?"

He said grimly he had thought so too. "We've all been hauled back. There's another flap on."

"Is there?" I told him about my lorries. "Do you know anything about them?"

He removed his cap and pushed his hand through his hair. "So that's who needs the billets."

"What billets?"

"I've just been told to produce billets for two hundred men in our chaps' barracks to-night. Must be for the chaps you saw come in. R.A.F., you say?"

I nodded unhappily. "Yes."

He looked at me. "I'd say they've knocked the fight out of

47

you, Clare. You apologized for knocking me over, and haven't attempted to black my eye. Am I right?"

"Yes. You're right."

"Brother Charles on your mind?" he asked not unkindly.

"Not only him—but mostly him."

He said conversationally, "Tell you something, young Clare. Never any point in beating your head against a wall of trouble. Gets you nothing but a headache. Tell you something else"—he took my bicycle from me and wheeled it through the arch towards the road—"if you find yourself getting het up over all this any time give me a ring. I'll buy you a fizzy lemonade, and have a damned fine row with you to take your mind off things." He glanced down at me. "What do you say? Why should we leave all the fighting to Jerry? Why can't you and I have a private war?"

I had to smile. "Mr Slaney, this is very big of you. Thanks."

He smiled back. "Big-hearted Joe, child. That's Slaney. Here." He held the bicycle steady. "Hop on, and I'll push you off."

"No, thanks." I took it from him. "I like scooting."

"Did you say you were twelve or twenty?" he called after me as I rode away.

I waved back, and returned to the V.A.D. Mess feeling slightly more cheerful, although I was not at all sure why. Once home I gave Madam her glasses, swopped a couple more platitudes about many hands making light work, and helped her lay the suppers. After supper I tried to ring my mother, as I needed the reassurance of her voice. I did not get it, as the girl on the exchange said there would be around five hours' delay for the call, and I could neither wait that long nor disturb my parents in the middle of the night just to say, "Hallo, this is Clare."

It grew very hot as the evening turned into night. In the Drawing-room we lay wakeful. The room was airless despite the open windows, and we talked quietly to each other. No one slept much that night. Just after eleven the convoys began again, and all night long the lorries thundered along the road beyond the tennis-courts. Once Mary went into the garden in her pyjamas. She came back after twenty minutes. She walked in wearily, the bright moonlight outlining her sturdy figure, and making her look like a tousle-haired child. "They're still the same," she told no one in particular, "full of men, sitting like sacks. They can't be wounded. I haven't seen one ambulance go by."

Miss Moreby-Aspin came in to early breakfast next morning. She looked very tired. "Members, I have a few changes to announce."

Janice Sims was one of the changes. Madam told her to go

straight to the Acute Surgical Block. "Frantly-Gibbs and Dillon will have to manage in Observation as best they can."

Mary and I exchanged glances. "The old girl looks out on her feet," murmured Mary.

Polly, the Home V.A.D., overheard. "Not surprising. She's been up since three." And she moved off with a pile of used plates before we could ask her more. I could not stay to wait for her return, as, being cycle-less, I had to leave breakfast early to allow for walking. Mary caught me up as I reached the hospital arch. "It seems, Clare dear," she announced, "that we can expect to find everything including the fairies at the bottom of the garden in the Ob. Block."

Beryl Jacks, the night V.A.D. in our Block, looked even more exhausted than Miss Moreby-Aspin. "You girls here already?" She thrust her untidy hair under her cap with a weary hand. "Thank God. I'm just about whacked."

Mary asked, "Beryl, have we got them in here?"

"Have we?" She smiled without humour. "For the record, girls, you've got twenty men in each ward. I've spent the night putting up beds and lifting sleeping men from the floor and shoving them into the beds."

I said, "Where are they from, Beryl?"

"France."

Mary and I asked together the question we were longing to ask, and dreading having answered. "Why?"

"Why?" She jerked her head at the door that connected the hall with the first ward. "They say—because we're retreating. They say our whole Army is on the run."

Mary stiffened, and suddenly altered from a friendly V.A.D. to a Regular soldier's wife. She was very much Mrs Major as she said sternly, "Don't talk such nonsense, Beryl. I simply won't believe it. Our Army never runs away."

Beryl shrugged. She was a small, thin girl, with a rabbity face—and she was dead tired. "Have it your own way, Frantly-Gibbs. I'm too damn tired to care who's running away from whom. I just want a bed—and I'm just repeating what they've told me. Walk into that ward if you want the truth." She swung her cloak over one shoulder. "I've written the report—such as it is—and I'm going to hang on until Sister comes. None of them are ill. They aren't patients. And now I'm going to get the hell out of it, in case another convoy comes in before I'm clear. If anyone asks me to heave another load of biscuits, or shove up another bed, I'll burst into tears. Good morning." She marched out.

Mary watched her go—and for the first and only time I saw Mary angry. "What the blazes does she think she's here for? To look pretty with that dirty great red cross on her apron? Oh

49

hell, Clare." She turned to me. "I don't believe any of this, but let's get it over."

The telephone bell interrupted us getting anything over. It was Matron's office. The office Sister told us Miss Thanet was already at work in the theatre, and would not be in the Block until later that morning. "Mrs Frantly-Gibbs must do the administration. Carry on with the routine as best you can. The M.O. will be there at his usual time to help you."

Mary sat down at the desk. "I'll have to read the report through first, Clare. You get started. I'll join you as soon as I've got a grip on what's come in."

"Right. Mary——"

"Yes?" She looked up from the report-book. She looked much older this morning. Older, and strained.

I said, "I'm sure Beryl's wrong. I'm sure your David is all right."

She forced a smile. "Thanks, Clare. I'll bet Charles is fine, too."

I returned her smile, and my smile felt as artificial as hers had looked. I walked alone to the doorway of the first ward, and the smile dropped from my face like an old coat from my back.

I stood in that doorway for a few seconds unnoticed by the men in the ward. They were all airmen. Their uniforms were very dirty, their faces a uniform greyish-white. It was the first time that I had seen close at hand the pallor that extreme physical fatigue gives to a healthy man; I have seen it a great many times since then, and each time I have been taken back to that lovely summer morning in the Ob. Block when I saw young men with faces like fungi sprawling all over the normally immaculate ward.

The men were very quiet; only two seemed to be asleep; the others lay silent on their beds, smoking and staring at the ceiling. A young corporal in the bed nearest to the door turned his head slowly and looked at me for perhaps a minute. He climbed off his bed, swung the rifle he had been nursing on to his shoulder, and came towards me. He was a very large man, with a round boy's face that was shadowed by an ill-grown beard. His eyes were not a boy's eyes; they looked old, and contrasted sharply with the rest of his face. "Nice little surprise packet for you," he said, in a slow West Country voice, "aren't we, Nurse?"

"Yes—er—you are." I made myself smile, and touched his rifle, clinging in this moment of shock to the security of routine regulations—as if those regulations could remove the touch of nightmare from the air. "How have you managed to keep your rifle, Corporal? The Army's pretty strict about weapons in hospital."

I watched his hand tighten on the butt of his rifle as he replied very politely, "Begging your pardon, Nurse—but I'd like to see anyone try and take it away from me."

Someone in the ward chuckled, and then I realized that every man present held either a rifle—or, even more strangely—an officer's revolver. The men, all awake now, had climbed off their beds and were gazing at me as if I appeared as unreal to them as they did to me. "As you've all got weapons," I said slowly, "I suppose you can't be patients?"

The men shook their heads, shuffled their feet, and looked at the corporal. He spoke for them. "That's right, Nurse. We've been just bedding down for the night. We're the first lot over. All the lads'll be back soon. We hope."

"All?"

Another man answered. "That's a fact, miss." He had a clipped Londoner's accent. He glanced at his companions, then went on, "It's this way, miss, like what the corporal said. We're the start—but the rest of the lads'll be along soon. You see, miss" —he hesitated—"well, it's this way—you see," he said again, "we're—on the run."

I looked from one weary face to another. They looked more than weary, they looked ashamed; and they avoided looking at me. "The R.A.F.—and the Army?" I did not think of Mary's husband or Charles. I did not dare think.

A man clutched my arm. His hand shook as he grasped me. "We been on the run across France for six days, miss—afore we got near the coast. We'd move to one place, see—build a new runway in a new field—and he'd find out and bomb it an' we'd have to shift again. So we shifts, see—builds another—and he finds that out, too. All the time we were going back—all the time—and he'd find out—and then—we couldn't go back any farther as we'd reached the sea. See?"

I nodded at his urgent face that was so near to mine. "Yes. I see."

The large corporal moved closer. "It were no good, Nurse. Charlie's right. Wherever we got—he got there too. Whenever we made a change—he knew about it."

The small Londoner said shrewdly, "It doesn't sound as if we done much good, miss, when he tells it, like. But we did what we could. Only it weren't enough. So we had to pack it in."

I could not ignore Charles any longer. I had to think of him and ask questions. "What squadrons are you from? Are all the R.A.F. back? What about the pilots?"

They looked at me now and shook their heads. The Londoner said they couldn't say, he was sure. I looked back at them, and realized that ambiguity would not help me to find out about Charles' squadron. They might be retreating men; they were not

51

defeated men. I recognized that. They were tired and depressed, but they were still fighting-men who would give no details away. I stopped trying to hedge and told them the truth. In a few moments I was in a ward full of brothers.

"He'll be home already, miss, sure he will!" they assured me heartily. "You don't want to worry about him, you don't! Pilots is valuable, so they got to look after them. Didn't they take that lot off in Blenheims—based in Wales, they said? You wait, miss —you see if your brother's not along of the Taffies, already! Soon as he's had a good kip down he'll be giving you a ring. You see if he don't!"

Their kindness was wonderful, but it could not quite reassure me, because I had seen the glances they had exchanged when I mentioned Charles' squadron number. I could not spend more time thinking and worrying about Charles, because they were now all talking at once.

The little Londoner talked the loudest. "I'll tell you what gives me a good headache, miss, an' that's me kit. Got a food parcel from my missus, I did, only last week. Sent me a cake she's made an' all—and I had to leave most of it to Jerry!"

The corporal said that was nothing to his loss. "What about them shoes my dad sent over for me? New shoes they were, Nurse—a fine good pair, and I had to leave them behind."

I sympathized with them both. "What rotten luck, I am sorry."

"You don't want to waste no sympathy on the corporal, miss!" retorted a chubby air-gunner. "It'll be the country what'll need your kind words. Think of the shocking name it'll get when Jerry finds them shoes and thinks as we've all got plates of meat that size. Talk about big! Cor! Needed a whole airstrip to himself to turn round in them, he did!"

The corporal laughed deeply. "When Jerry catches sight of them pictures of Betty Grable you been hanging up he'll have other things to think on, Charlie, besides—oh!——" He broke off sharply, as someone kicked him hard. "Begging your pardon, Nurse, I am that. I'm afraid I was forgetting myself."

I smiled, feeling only too thankful to Miss Grable for lightening the moment. "That's all right, Corporal. I think she's smashing too. She was on at the camp cinema last week." I shook my head, as if the movement would clear my mind. I knew that there was so much I must do for these tired, kind young men, only I did not know where to start. Then I looked at their beards. "Have any of you got any razors?"

They had not one razor between them.

The corporal fingered his beard. "Be nice to have a shave and a clean-up, miss."

"Right." I looked round, and they smiled at me hopefully,

and with a wonderful trust in all their faces, as if I could provide the answer to all they needed to ask. "What about soap? No?" I thought of our small stores, and decided that was something else over which I must not waste time in thought. "All right. I'll fix something for you all directly. First I'll just nip through the other wards and see how the other newcomers are."

The corporal asked diffidently, "Could we be doing something to help you, Nurse?"

I was going to refuse, on the grounds that they were far too tired to help anyone, when I read the appeal in his eyes. I looked at the other men. The corporal's expression was mirrored in nineteen other pairs of eyes. "Could you get this ward clean for me? You will? Oh, bless you all!" I raced off for a broom, dusters, biscuit-tins, scrubbing-brush, scouring powder, floor-polish, and bumper. They leapt to take the cleaning tools from me, as if I was offering them gold. "And there's the fire in that hall there. Could you get it going for me?"

They said there was nothing they liked so much as lighting fires. "Be a pleasure, Nurse. We'll give this a good clean-up for you. Got any Brasso? Ta. Here—Bert—you got that bit of shammy you scrounged from that dead Jerry? Let's have it, mate. Ta."

I went back to Mary. "Did you hear any of that?"

She smiled slightly. "I heard. Thanks, Clare."

I could not linger; I went quickly through the six remaining wards, and six times that first scene was repeated; six times I discovered a razorless and soapless ward, filled with dirty, unshaven men; six times I was inundated with offers to clean, scrub, and polish. With the Block buzzing with energy, I returned to Mary.

She had news for me. "The Ass. Mat.'s just been round to see if we were under control. I said we were. The Block has to be ready by nine. No clean beds. All these men are going this morning. How are you doing?"

I told her. "I must have razors and more soap. Can I go scrounging?"

"Go where you like. What about baths?"

The airman lighting the fire looked up at that last word. He looked as if Mary had mentioned the keys of Heaven. "Did you say baths, miss? For us?"

Mary smiled. "If we can raise them." She nodded at me. "Try Sister D.S."

"I will. I'll go there first." I raced up the iron staircase and along the balcony. Sister Dirty Surgical received my somewhat breathless request calmly. "Miss Dillon, I have eighty men up here. You'll never be able to fit your men in. But you may try."

I thanked her gratefully, tore down the balcony and stairs and across to the Orthopædic Block. Sister O.B. gave me permission to send a dozen men over to use her bathrooms. "No more, as I'll need them for my own men."

I was growing desperate when I remembered the missing T.B. patients in the Acute Medical Block. Sister A.M. said she had never heard such an absurd request in her life. "I can't have healthy men tramping up and down my Block. You'll have to tell your men to be very quiet, Miss Dillon—and if they see anyone who looks like an M.O., tell them to cough, and try and look sick."

I thanked her. "They look sick all right, Sister."

Sister A.M. was a Scot; a stern disciplinarian and a very nice woman. Her face altered. "The poor laddies," she said, "you can send them here. As many as you wish, provided they are quiet. I've no up-patients at all, and nine bathrooms."

Flushed with triumph, I raced next to the Pack Store. "Staff, how many razors, towels, and how much soap can you give me? Off form?"

For the only time in my Army life Staff Williams failed me. He had no razors. He loaded me with soap and towels. "What the Q.M.'ll say to me for this, Miss Dillon, I wouldn't like to say. That be enough?"

"I'm sure it will. Bless you, Staff. You're an angel!"

I went back to the Ob. Block and briefed the large corporal. He took the soap and towels, promised to organize the bath-queues, and make certain that the men going to the Medical Block produced graveyard coughs. In the hall Mary was serving breakfast, and being assisted by about fifty men, who bore a close resemblance to characters in a Hollywood horse-opera. "Any luck with razors?" she asked.

"Not a single blade. No one seems to have any," but as I spoke I had an inspiration. "Can I use the 'phone?"

She raised her eyebrows. "Go ahead. Got a corner somewhere?"

"One worth trying." I picked up the receiver. "Corporal Jenkins, can you get me Mr Slaney?"

"Lieut. Slaney's in Casualty, miss. He's only taking urgent calls."

"This one's urgent, Corporal. Put me through—there's a dear. I'll take the rap."

He chuckled. "If you say so, miss."

Joe's voice sounded on the line almost at once. "Slaney here. What is it?"

I did not waste words either. "This is the Ob. Block. Can we please borrow your razor, Mr Slaney? And as many more as you can raise?"

There was a small silence. Then he said curtly, "Miss Dillon, I'm very busy. Did you bother me only for that?"

"I'm busy, too!" I snapped. "We've got one hundred and forty unshaven men here and no razor. You're our M.O. You told me to ring you if I wanted anything. I do. Your razor and spare blades."

He made a sound that was half a grunt, half a laugh. "I'll have a selection of both sent over," he said, and rang off.

Two hours later the Ob. Block was full of clean, smoothly shaven men, who had breakfasted enormously on porridge, eggs, bread, butter, and tea; the wards shone with an equal cleanliness; the floors were like glass; the lamp-shades spotless; the lockers scrubbed white; the brasses burnished to gold.

Sister returned to us at half-past nine. She rolled up her sleeves, pinned back her shoulder cape, and left Mary and me gasping at the speed she suddenly produced as she went about her work. She also looked much happier than we had ever seen her; she had done four hours' work in the theatre before rejoining us, but she did not look at all tired. Her cheeks were pink, her eyes shining with pleasure at being able to do what she called "real work" at last.

She told us that all our men were to parade on the square at midday to be ready to move off. "As soon as they've gone off start stripping all the beds and then make them up clean."

Before the men left every man shook hands with Sister, Mary, and myself. They gave Mary and me their cap-badges and bits of insignia as farewell tokens; the large corporal took me to one side and furtively handed me the first piece of shrapnel I had seen.

"Thought you might like it as a curio, miss." He lowered his voice conspiratorially, and added, "Could you be coming into the first ward, please? The lads are wanting to see you."

There were many more than the twenty occupants waiting in that ward. When the corporal led me in the men moved their feet as if embarrassed, smiled sheepishly, then thrust forward one young Yorkshireman. He grinned at me, and turned purple. He wanted, he said, to say a few words on behalf of "t'lads." The lads nodded, and looked at him expectantly, but he had lost his nerve. He turned a deeper shade of purple, and pushed a vast box of Naafi chocolates into my unexpecting hands. "Appreciation—Nurse—we're reet grateful—t'lads and me—and we—hope as your brother——" He was too shy to go on; he simply stared at me dumbly while I clutched my chocolates, stared back, and felt my eyes pricking, and then without warning the tears rolled down my face and I could do nothing to stop them. The corporal patted my shoulder in a fatherly way, and the men near to me smiled agonizingly.

"I felt such a fool and so ashamed," I told Sister and Mary later as we shared the chocolates. "I hadn't done anything but find soap and rustle up a few razors, and they were acting as if I had nursed them tenderly for weeks."

Sister said soberly, "You were the first human being they met, Dillon. They must have been dreading meeting you." She looked at me and gave a curious little smile. "You were their mums, their wives, their girl friends, for them this morning. In fact—you were England. That's true. I expect they'll remember you for a long time."

"But they met Jacks last night?"

"Last night they were too tired to care. This morning was different. Now let's get on with those beds. I'll give you a hand."

When the beds were done we straightened our aching backs. Sister asked, "Have either of you seen a paper yet?"

We said no. "Anything new in them, Sister?"

"Nothing. Just the usual about strategic retreats and everything going according to plan. I thought you'd like to know."

That afternoon we filled up again, this time with soldiers, who were graded 'walking wounded.' Over half our new patients were French. Sister asked Mary and me if we spoke their language. "I'm hopeless at more than the gardener's cat."

I said I knew little more than that, but Mary was fluent.

Sister told Mary to deal with the Frenchmen. "Keep them in the last four wards. Dillon, put the English into the first three." She sat down at her desk. "I must get their papers straight, then I'll come and help you both. Give them all tea and cigarettes before you do anything else. I've put out boxes of cigarettes and matches on the kitchen table. Then each of you start in one corner of a ward, help them wash, into bed, and work round. If anyone needs a dressing put on a clean, dry dressing until the M.O. or I get to him." She smiled at us both; she was an experienced friend, and not an aloof Sister to-day. "Sorry there won't be any off-duty to-day, but you wouldn't take it if I gave it you. Off you go—and if you set eyes on Mr Slaney or any M.O. say I'm in here."

Mary asked, "Has Mr Slaney been round at all? I've only seen Major Endsby in here."

Sister explained that Joe Slaney had taken residence in Casualty. "They've been admitting since midnight last night. I don't think any M.O.'s got to bed—and by the look of it they won't to-night, either."

The soldiers were tired, but much more talkative than the men this morning. They talked mostly about the R.A.F., and they talked bitterly. "Hear as you had the Brylcreem Boys in this morning, Nurse? Trust the boys in blue to get out of the scrap first! Don't know what we got a R.A.F. for, Nurse—I don't, and no mistake! Not seen one of our planes for days, we haven't. But Jerry—he was there all the time. *Wheeeee!*" The soldier I was washing yelled suddenly in his impersonation of a dive-bomber. We heard a lot of those yells as the days went on, but this was the first I heard. "Down he'd come," the soldier continued, "like a bat out of hell—and he'd keep on coming. But the R.A.F.! Strike a light, Nurse! We didn't never see them! What we says is, thank Gawd we got a Navy!"

I could not answer him, or his colleagues who repeated his story, as I did not know the answer, and they were too bitter to be put off with invented explanations. Later Miss Thanet discussed this when she joined me as I cut the tea bread.

"I'll spread while you cut." She buttered the bread swiftly. "Have you heard what they're saying about the R.A.F.?"

She did not know about Charles. I said, "Yes. They sound pretty mad."

She nodded. "I'll say. Seems awfully queer, though; there must have been some of our planes somewhere. But all this talk ties up with what I heard this morning."

"What was that, Sister?"

"I heard"—she laid a plate with buttered bread as she spoke —"that they had to shift those men we had in out quickly, as the Army was coming in, and they didn't want to risk mixing the two Services just now. Tempers are running high." She asked about Mary's husband. "He's a soldier, isn't he? Over there?"

"Yes. He's a major in a Rifle Regiment."

She grimaced. "Poor girl. Any children?"

"No."

"Poor girl," she said again. "Must be hell for her. I haven't liked to ask her anything, but I could see she's all buttoned-up to-day. Let me know if she hears anything."

"Yes, Sister."

She glanced at me. "Have you got a young man across the water?"

I cut the bread more fiercely. "My twin brother. He's a pilot officer. On bombers. He's meant to be flying one of those aeroplanes that don't appear to have been flying."

She put down her knife momentarily. "My God, Dillon—I am sorry. If I'd known that I would not have said what I said."

I thanked her, and told her not to worry. "I've been hearing it, too, all afternoon."

After tea the Assistant Matron appeared in our hall. "Sister, I believe Mrs Frantly-Gibbs speaks fluent French? She does? Splendid. I want her to act as interpreter in the Acute Blocks. The M.O.'s must have help. Can you and Miss Dillon manage alone here?"

Sister said we could manage very well. "It wouldn't have made any difference if I had said we couldn't, Dillon," she added afterwards, "but it sounded better that way. Let's get them all settled for supper, then I'll have to get on with my report, as it's going to be a mammoth one to-night, and you'll have to cope with suppers on your own. Don't let the men help, even if they offer. They're far too tired to do anything to-night."

I had to re-lay and light the fire that had died from lack of attention that afternoon, before I started the suppers. Sister watched unmoved as I emptied the polish-tin and then threw on a couple of rags soaked in meth. to get the fire going. Joe joined her while I was reheating the baked beans and tea, which for once was cold, since I had not been free to serve it directly it arrived, and the cookhouse orderly had been too pressed to carry the bucket beyond the hearth.

Sister and Joe did a thorough medical round, as I scampered up and down the seven wards with plates of baked beans, rather soggy toast, and very hot, if over-stewed, tea. I had to wake each man before he ate; some men were too weary to feed themselves, and those I fed. The majority of these were exhausted, shocked Frenchmen, who stared blankly at me as I coaxed baked beans and tea into them, and murmured, "Merci, Mademoiselle," and dropped back to sleep again before I left their bedside.

I piled our largest tray with as many dirty plates and mugs as it would hold, and returned to the hall to find Joe alone at the desk. He looked up from his writing.

"Get your chaps shaved?"

"Yes, thanks." I put the tray on the floor and rubbed my back absently. "Those razors are clean and on the surgery table if you want to take them back."

"If I don't there'll be the devil of a number of bearded M.O.'s on the staff to-morrow. I told my batman to swipe the lot." He noticed my tray. "You'll give yourself a hernia if you carry weights like that. Why not stagger the load?"

"My father says women seldom get ruptures. My inside'll hold out. My feet won't. I'd rather carry a mountain, and save my feet an extra journey."

He stood up slowly, as if not only his feet but every bone in his body was aching. "What will you do with that lot?"

"Take it into the scullery to wash up."

"The scullery? Oh, you mean the sink cupboard." He lifted the tray from the floor. "You must be an exceedingly tough young woman, even if you don't look it." He carried the tray into the minute cupboard that we graced with the name of scullery, and laid it on the draining-board. "Either that"—he leant against the door—"or I'm getting old."

Something in his voice made me look at him closely. I had been too busy to do that before that evening. He did not look old, he did not look deathly tired, he just looked like death. His face was as grey as the men's this morning, and his whole body was wilting against the door as if his bones were turning to water. I said, "Are you all right? What have you been doing? You look frightfully queer." As he did not answer I hauled a chair forward. "Look here, sit down and I'll heat you some tea. There's a little left, and you always like the dregs."

He did not even respond to that. He merely gazed at me and blinked. "Hold it," he said at last, without moving, "and stop panicking. I'm O.K. Don't waste your time brewing me tea. You've enough on your plate. There's nothing at all the matter with me. It must be the light playing tricks that makes me look queer."

"If you're sure——" I began uncertainly, then, before I could say anything else, he dropped on to the floor as heavily as if I had taken a mallet and knocked him on the head. He lay quite still and limp, like a puppet doll that had been thrown down by a bored child.

4

AND STILL THEY COME

I SQUATTED by his unconscious figure, wishing that Sister had not disappeared. I tried hard to recollect all I had been taught in our first-aid lectures; my brain remained uncomfortably blank and Joe Slaney remained on the floor in front of me. His colour was shocking; he was so pale that for a few wild seconds I thought he was dead. I had never seen anyone dead then, and I did not know the unmistakable waxy pallor of death. I touched his face gingerly, and felt his breath on my hand as I did so. I was infinitely relieved. Relief brought back my scattered common sense, and the teachings I had received in those lectures. I undid his tie, and loosened his collar and belt.

He opened his eyes. "The technique, woman, is to stand well back and holler for a doctor. If that doesn't work raise the feet to increase the flow of blood to the head."

I sat back on my heels. "Shall I do that?"

He smiled up at me. "Over my dead body." He raised himself on one elbow. "The boy is himself again. How about that tea you offered me?"

"Oughtn't it to be brandy? You're an awful colour."

"Tea. Just tea." He got to his feet unsteadily. "Never give unconscious characters alcohol. Bad scheme, that—unless you're certain as to the cause of their passing out. If you shove alcohol down someone at random, and they are having an internal hæmorrhage, you really do let the cat loose among the pigeons." He swayed dangerously. "When in doubt stick to tea."

I was too concerned by his appearance to pay much attention to what he was saying.

"Hey." I put my hands on either side of his waist. "You'll pass out again if you aren't careful. Lean on me—it's all right, I can take your weight—I've supported heavier men than you. That's it. Lean on my shoulders and I'll shove you slowly back into that chair behind you. Good. Sit down, now." He dropped his hands from my shoulders as he flopped into the chair and folded them in his lap like an obedient child. "Just you stay sitting there, Mr Slaney, sir, and don't get up until I've got you that tea."

The fire was glowing; reheating the remains in the tea-bucket took only a few moments. I stirred in five teaspoonfuls of sugar.

"Be like syrup, I'm afraid, but my father says too sweet tea makes a splendid stimulant."

The ghost of a smile flickered over his haggard face. "Yes, miss. Just as you say. I won't give no more trouble." His colour returned to normal as he swallowed the scalding liquid. "This is all very competent, Clare. Where did you learn all this?"

"From our lectures—my father—all mixed up. But I wasn't at all competent when you passed out. I was scared stiff."

"Were you now?" He looked into his mug. "That makes two of us."

I said, "Joe, what happened?"

He looked up. "I fainted."

"I know that. But—why?"

His expression was guarded. "People do faint."

"I know that too. But why did you?"

He grinned. "I had the vapours. I was seized all of a tremble. It's a terrible thing—I eats well, I drinks well, I sleeps well. But when it comes to a job of work I go all of a tremble. That's all."

I did not smile. "I'm not Madam. Don't quote corn to me. I really want to know. What's wrong with you? Why did you faint? Healthy young men don't faint."

"Oh, hell." He stood up. "So they don't? Well, I do. I pass out at the drop of a hat. As you saw. Now I'm back again, and I've the devil of a lot of work to do."

I watched him walk to the table. He certainly looked better, but he still looked ill. Have you got a weak heart?"

"Oh, sure, sure. It's aching and breaking—and all"—he produced a magnificent brogue—"for the love of you! Now will you just relax, Clare Dillon, and leave a man to get on with his work. And—er—if you could forget this little episode, I'll be damned grateful to you. Not that I'll forget—but I'd like it if you would."

I hesitated. "You ought to tell someone. You ought to see——"

"A doctor? Sure, I'll see a doctor. In hell, first." He looked at me steadily. "Will you listen to me and just stop flapping? I've told you that there's nothing wrong with me; that I just fainted—maybe because I was tired. I'm fine now. And I'm damned if I'm having any more talk about my little lapse on an evening like this. Hell, Clare, be your age! The hospital's fit to bursting with real patients. What would I want to bother anyone with my fit of the vapours for?"

"All right. If you say so. You're the doctor. But I still don't like it, and when this flap's over, I do think you ought to tell someone."

He said softly, "And what makes you think this flap'll be over? Girl, it's just started."

Sister came in as he spoke. "I'm so sorry, Mr Slaney, I was kept in the office. I hope you've been managing all right alone."

He beamed at her. "I've managed fine." He did not look my way. "Come and take a seat, Sister, and let's get these admission forms signed. How many hundred have we admitted to-day? Tell me all. In triplicate."

It was dark before I got off duty that night. Beryl Jacks lent me her cycle and I rode slowly back to our Mess feeling grateful for the darkness, after the eternal sunshine of this summer. I tried to think of Charles; I was too tired; I was too tired to wonder any longer why Joe had fainted; too tired to think of anything. I only wanted to fall on a bed and drop asleep, or so I thought, until I went to bed. Once there I was too weary for sleep. I lay and looked at the grey shadows the night made on the ceiling of the Drawing-room, and thought about men with grey faces; I wondered if Charles was in some hospital to-night, and whether his face was grey too, or whether he was lying somewhere as limply as Joe Slaney had lain on the duty-room floor that evening, and if his face was not grey, but a waxen, greenish-white.

Mary was not sleeping either. She raised her head as she heard my bed creak. "Let's go outside and get some air, Clare." She climbed quietly out of bed, pulled her hospital cloak from her chair, and tip-toed in bare feet to the nearest french windows. I found my own cloak, remembered cigarettes and matches, and followed her out. We walked over the lawn and the first tennis-court, and lay on the sloping bank that was at the far end of that court. Mary folded her arms behind her head. "The grass is still warm." She changed her position and took a cigarette. "I wonder," she murmured, lighting it, "where David is to-night?"

"What date was on that last trio of letters?"

"They varied. The most recent was ten days old." She looked my way.

"How about Charles?"

"About ten days, I think."

The night was clear, the air very soft. There was no wind, not even a faint breeze, and nothing stirred in the garden. There was only one small transparent cloud in the sky; it hung just below the moon like a dropped pearl. We did not speak for some time; in the silence I heard far off the short scream of a terrified rabbit, and once the hoarse bark of a fox.

Mary said suddenly, "I wonder if this is the end of the beginning, or the beginning of the end? Does that sound corny? It doesn't stop me wondering even if it does."

I waved the smoke of her second cigarette away from my face, and wished I could as easily wave the thoughts from my mind.

"It's all corny," I said, "sheer corn. Or has been until now.

62

To-day. I've felt all the time as if I've been part of an act left over from the last war. I've felt some smug little Red Cross Heroine in a movie, with my long skirt and black stockings and red crosses embroidered all over me. I've even got a fine handsome twin brother at what has up till now been a non-existent Front. I've known all about me and exactly how I ought to behave because I've read all the books and seen all the movies."

"And now?"

I sat up and looked down at her as she lay, a shadow in the shadows, with one pin-point of light glowing to mark her face. "Now I'm out of my depth. I don't know how to behave. Do you?"

She lay still. "How to behave when you face a retreating army? No, I don't. I don't know what to say or do. Either this morning or to-night."

"With your Frenchmen?"

"Not so much with them. It was with one of our own men. A R.A.F. boy who was left behind in Acute Surgical because he was too bad to be moved. I heard him crying behind his screens, when I was translating for Archie Oliver. As soon as I could I went round his screens. He hung on to my apron and wept into the skirt. I had to borrow a clean one from Sylvia Frant. He was only a kid. He cried and cried." She was silent for several seconds. "We had a baby once. A boy. If he had lived he would have been able to fight in this war soon. He'd have been fifteen now."

I was so surprised and saddened for her, that momentarily I forgot the present.

"Mary—I'm desperately sorry. What happened? Or would you rather not talk?"

She sat up then and watched, as I was watching a new convoy of lorries drive along the road that was a silver ribbon in the moonlight. "May as well talk to-night. There's nothing else to do." She turned towards me. "It was years ago. He was born the year after we were married; he died when he was two. He got pneumonia and died." Her voice cracked slightly. "Poor little Dave. He was such a fat little boy—and such fun. We never had another. I don't know why not. We wanted children."

"Mary—I am so sorry," I said again, because there was nothing else I could say.

She sighed, not unhappily, but as if she were waking from sleep. "It's all so long ago now that it seems to belong to a different person in a different life. It's as if I'm talking of someone else's baby, not mine. It was hell when it happened; worse hell than I ever could imagine. I didn't know anything could hurt like that."

63

"I've heard that's so. 'What do you know of grief, you who have not lost a child?' "

She twisted her head sharply to me. "Who said that?"

"Marcus Aurelius. My father told me. It was when one of his child-patients died. He was terribly upset."

"Child-patients—— Of course, he's a doctor." She lay back on the warm grass again. "That quotation's right; quite right. After Dave nothing has ever really hurt again."

I said, "Mary, I think you're rather wonderful. I honestly do. I never guessed that anything bad had happened to you. I didn't even think that you and David had been married long."

"My good child, I've been married over sixteen years." She sounded amused. "I'm thirty-seven. David's a year older. He's pretty old for his rank, but he isn't a very good soldier. In fact, he's a lousy soldier, poor darling. He's not at all martial, and he's no head for details. If the War hadn't been looming ahead this last couple of years he'd have been on the retired list soon. I wonder," she added slowly, "if he's still alive."

I looked at her, and thought about what she had just told me. "Isn't it agony for you, Mary? Worrying?"

"No. Unless you call a toothache agony. I don't. I call it a nagging ache; worry's the same, when it's constant. And I know it won't be constant for long."

"You've got a hunch you're going to hear from David soon?"

"Not that. Merely on past showing. Nothing ever lasts, Clare. Good or bad, nothing lasts. David and I have had a lot of fun together—we've been luckier than kids like you—we managed to get our fun at the right age. We had rows, too; hundreds of them, particularly after little Dave died, and we were both near scream-ing-point with our despair. Then we settled down!"—her voice sounded as if she was smiling—"we jogged along like most married couples do, and although that may sound dull at your age, it isn't. I can't wish you anything better, Clare, than that when this rubbish is over you'll be able to jog along with some good man." She laughed quietly. "There's a Victorian statement for you! And why not, as I'm talking about goodness in the old-fashioned sense of the word? It's a rare quality in a man; kind-ness is even more rare. David's kind. He never makes a fuss about not wanting to hurt people, he just doesn't hurt them. Which is why he's such a rotten soldier. He detests killing."

"What made him become a regular soldier?"

"His father was a brigadier. David just drifted into the Army automatically. Once in he hadn't the energy to get out. It would have meant a family row as well as everything else. He sampled one of those when he married me; he was officially too young to marry then; his colonel was pretty decent about it, his father was hell. Luckily David had some money of his own his mother left

64

him, so we didn't have to rely on my father-in-law for that, and he came around in time."

I said, "Charles must be something like David. He's nuts on flying, but he loathes killing."

She yawned. "Someone must, or we wouldn't be here now. To-night's original thought. We'd better go in to bed, Clare. It'll be dawn soon." She stood up stiffly. "Wonder what to-morrow will be like?"

The next day, and the days that followed, were so exactly like that previous day that the period seemed timeless, and the only constant facts in our lives were the sun, our personal anxieties, and our aching feet. The hospital filled, emptied, filled, emptied again, to the great civilian war hospitals inland; those of us who spoke only school-room French found our knowledge of that language became much improved as we discussed *les avions allemands*; *les bombardements*; and *les* 'dive-bombers—*zut alors*!' Our French-speaking patients—and these now included some North African troops—quickly learnt a mixed Anglo-American-hospital-barrack slang, and loved nothing better than trying out this strange, but perfectly intelligible, language on us.

One morning I handed a mug of cocoa to a very young Frenchman. He made a charming little bow from his waist as he sat up in bed; "I am thanking ye kindly, ye Goddamn nurse."

Our own troops in that ward were horrified. The Geordie lance-corporal in the next bed bounced up sternly. "And have ye no bluidy manners at all, man, to use such language to the nurse?"

The British troops were now beyond horror. They gazed at Geordie in united disapproval, and I had to grimace hideously to control my facial muscles. They would have been even more shocked had I been caught smiling. The men would not countenance even the mildest oath being used in the presence of a Sister or nurse. As Mary said, "Really, dear, they are such a strain, as I have to watch my language all the time." It was only in the officers' wards that we heard in ordinary conversation the four-letter words that are reputed to be written on the walls in gentlemen's lavatories.

That morning I distributed the rest of the cocoa to a silent ward and avoided looking at Geordie's apologetic, purple face, or the astonished, slightly pathetic expression worn by his next-door bed neighbour, who had no idea what he had said, but had grasped from the atmosphere, and Geordie's tone, that he had committed some unforgivable sin.

Fortunately just then Geordie chanced to look through the window behind his bed. "Will ye take a look at this little lot, Nurse! Seems there's a packet coming in!"

The up-patients crowded round the windows with me and watched the slow, apparently endless line of ambulances creep in under the hospital arch. Mary appeared beside me. "Not more Frenchmen, please," she murmured. "I can't take any more interpreting. It gives me too much time for standing and staring."

Sister joined us a few minutes later. "Casualty have just rung. We've to take twenty men. The Pack Store are bringing over extra bedsteads and biscuits."

Staff Williams spoke to me when he deposited his final load of iron on the hall floor. "Between you and me, miss," he said, flexing his shoulders, "this is about the last bedstead in the camp. If they don't shift them Frogs out soon we'll have to put our own lads on the floor."

I was surprised. "Are the French due to be shifted, Staff? I hadn't heard."

He pulled his left ear-lobe. "That's as may be, miss. But you mark my words. They'll not mix 'em in here with our lads much longer."

I stacked three biscuits and lifted them together. "Why?"

His lined face was thoughtful. "Seems as if asking for your cards is catching like, miss. So the lads as are coming back now says." He tucked an iron bed-head under each arm. "Where's the Sister wanting these beds fixed? Down the centre of the wards, like as before?"

"Please. But, Staff—one moment—who's asking for their cards now? Surely the French aren't giving in?"

"You talked to the lads, miss?"

I nodded.

"Well, miss, then you can't hardly say as them Frogs are holding out, can you?" He did not wait for an answer. He marched stolidly into the first ward, put down the bed-heads, and returned for the foot rails and the springs.

Joe walked into the hall while we were serving lunches. He walked heavily, like an old man. He looked so ill that once again I was convinced he had a weak heart. I had discussed this with Mary when I told her about his faint. She had agreed that there was something wrong with Joe, but doubted that what was wrong concerned his heart. "He's not got a cardiac colour. He hasn't any colour at all. And if he gets any thinner his cheek-bones will break through the skin of his face. Yet there can't really be anything much wrong with him, Clare," she had added. "He manages the work all right. No man who was really ill could work as our M.O.'s are working these days. They'll pass out—and stay passed out."

Joe walked up to Sister, who was dishing out the stew. "Got a moment, Sister?"

She held the ladle poised as she smiled at him. "No, Mr Slaney." She and Joe were on amicable terms now they had faced so many problems together. "Have I got to make one?"

"You have." He crossed to her desk and sat down. "We've got to shift all the French that can be moved. Which means eighty per cent of ours. We have got to produce beds for our own chaps. They're all on their way back."

"All?" Sister, Mary, and I spoke together.

He leant one elbow on the table and supported his head with his hand, as if his neck was too weary to bear the weight any longer. "All who can swim," he said gently, "so they tell me." The telephone in front of him rang. He reached for the receiver. "Slaney. Observation. Who?" He looked at Mary. "Yes, she's here. Hold it—what? Will I tell her you haven't time but will ring her later? I will." He smiled at Mary. "Congratulations." He replaced the receiver and stood up. "That was a chap called David Frantly-Gibbs. He wanted to tell you he's fine, in a hurry, and will try and call you later." He had walked round the table now and was confronting Mary, who stood clutching a plate of stew. He removed the plate from her unresisting hands. "Well, now, and why would you want to weep tears into that when it'll be too salt already?" He patted her shoulder with his free hand. "Can you raise a drop of brandy for the lady, Sister? She looks as if she could do with it—and not only in celebration."

The controlled Mary was sobbing unashamedly over the medicine glass of brandy a couple of minutes later. "I never realized I was scared until now, when there's no more need to be scared."

Joe returned to the desk. "That always happens when you sit on a fear. It ups and hits you below the belt when it's all over." He glanced at me as he spoke, and his expression was very kind. This did not surprise me, for during this last couple of weeks or so we had all had the opportunity to discover that when Joe Slaney was too busy or too tired to be affected the kindly streak in his make-up, on which he had previously sat as firmly as Mary had sat on her fears for David, came to the surface. I knew exactly why he glanced at me like that; now we all knew each other so much better David Frantly-Gibbs and Charles Dillon were invisible members of the Ob. Block day staff. Some time afterwards, during that lunch period, when I returned for the pudding jam, I heard Sister ask him, "Do you think there's any hope for that girl's brother?" He had seen me come in. He did not answer.

Staff Williams stopped me in the square when I went to my own lunch. He was beaming. "My boy's back, miss! He just give me a call. At Upper Weigh, he is! Think of that!

Seems as they're sorting their lads out there! Heard from your brother?"

"Not yet, Staff. There may be a message waiting at our Mess. I'm so pleased about your son!"

His eyes were alight with relief. "It's been on me mind, miss, I can tell you. His mum'll be glad, too. He's our only lad. You keep your chin up about your brother, miss. He'll be back. You see."

"I hope you're right, Staff." I told him about Mary's husband. "That's good news, too."

He was delighted for Mary. "There now. That Mrs Frantly-Gibbs'll be on top of the world, I reckon. A real nice lady is that Mrs Frantly-Gibbs. What I call a proper lady, and no side to her, for all her gentleman's a major. That just goes to show, Miss Dillon. Your brother'll make the third. Everything always goes in threes, it does."

"I hope so, Staff. I really do. Thanks."

We had thought the hospital very busy up to that time; that evening we discovered our previous admissions had been a mere trickle in comparison to what then arrived, and continued to arrive for the next few days. During those days every Sister and nurse in the hospital was occupied washing the earth of France—the sand from Dunkirk, the dirt from Saint-Malo, Brest, and Cherbourg—the oil from wrecked ships, and the salt from the Channel from the weary, wounded bodies of the men of our own Army. As we washed and dressed those men we listened to what they said as they relaxed for the first time. Those soldiers talked and talked; they talked long before they had the chance to read a newspaper or listen to a wireless bulletin; they talked before they had any chance to compare notes with each other, or spin the stories which later would become legends; and they talked as freely as people will only talk to their nurses. They had many accents, but only one voice; and that voice said the same thing. "So Froggie's going to pack it in, eh, Nurse? Oh, well. He weren't much use. Be better now we're on our own. We'll know where we are, like."

It was a day or so later that the loudspeakers in the corners of the ward crackled to life as Mary and I were serving cocoa. The assorted troops lying in bed looked expectantly at the loudspeakers as, in English, we heard the news of the French capitulation. When the announcement was over a Green Howard sergeant said quietly, "That's that."

There were three Frenchmen in that ward. They had been too ill to be moved out with their compatriots. The English-speaking men glanced at the Frenchmen and were silent. One Frenchman looked at Mary. He had not understood the announcement. He asked her to translate.

The Green Howard sergeant nodded. "Best tell them, Nurse. They got to know some time." But before she had to say a word the news was repeated in French. Again the ward listened in silence, and when that announcement was over they remained silent, and the silence was broken only by one of the three French soldiers who began to cry. For the rest of that day that one ward in the Ob. Block was filled to capacity with dumb men who avoided each other's eyes and buried themselves in *Razzle*.

The remaining six wards, having no Frenchmen in their midst, were anything but silent. There was a relieved, almost gay—seconds out of the ring—atmosphere. One sapper whom I washed that evening said this news was going to be a reg'lar tonic for his old dad. "Proper made up he's been ever since he joined the L.D.V.! Reckons as he's fighting Jerry single-handed now, he does! He ain't half going to be bucked about this! I tell you, Nurse, he was real narked last year when they told him as he was too old for this do!"

"I'm glad he's going to enjoy himself." I smiled at the sapper, who had bad facial injuries and dangled his uninjured hand in my basin of hot water. Your face hurt much?"

"Nah. Ta." He winked above his bandages. "Reckon as they'll call me Scarface when I gets back home. I won't half put the wind up Jerry with my physog if he comes over!" He dabbled his fingers in the water. "This feels good, Nurse."

"That's nice." When I dried his hand I asked, "Think Jerry's going to try and invade us now?"

"I dunno. But I tell you what, Nurse—I wouldn't half like to see him try!" He raised his voice to shout over the screen separating his bed from the ward. "Oy! Robin Hood! You think Jerry'll try and have a bash over here, mate?"

The Sherwood Forester on the other side of the screen guffawed. "That'll be the day? Eh, Bert?"

I asked, "You think we can hold out?"

The now listening ward did not bother to think about this. "Course we will, Nurse! We'll sock him—'cause we blooming well got to—if you'll pardon the word, Nurse!"

That ward spoke for the Ob. Block, and the Ob. Block, according to our fellow-V.A.D.'s, spoke for the hospital. Just let the bastard try—begging your pardon, miss—and he'll find what he could do with his something dive-bombers, his something something machine-gunning pilots who used unarmed refugees as target practice, and his something something bag of Fifth Column tricks. Just—let—him—try.

A wounded R.A.M.C. orderly in the end bed smiled dreamily as I screened his bed to wash him. "He's a cunning one, though, Nurse. Got to hand it to him. We was evacuating some of our wounded over there, see. We had 'em on stretchers, and was getting 'em into a lorry. We sees a couple of lads coming across the field towards us in Froggie uniform—so we stops to wait for them, seeing as them two lads has a stretcher between them. We waits. They gets quite near us, then they puts down their stretcher, seemingly as if they was tired and had to rest. They even smiles and nods, like, as they stretches their arms. And then up pops the Jerry what's been lying doggo under the blanket. He's got a Tommy in his hands, and he lets us have it—proper." He laughed softly. "Thought as he'd fix us, he did; only he didn't reckon on two of our lads as was standing in the back of that lorry picking up the machine-gun what we didn't ought to have by rights, us being non-com. Our lads finishes them three Jerries off pronto, but first we lost five of our lads, and that's where I picks up this packet in me legs. Still, fair's fair," he added reasonably, "and you got to hand it to Jerry. He knew as he might cop it—he took the chance. Jerry's got guts all right."

"Is Miss Dillon there?" Sister's voice came over the screen. Her tone was urgent and glad. I shot around the screen quickly. "Yes, Sister?"

She was looking radiant, the way people do look when they bring good news. "Your twin brother has just been on the telephone. He didn't say where he was, only to tell you he's back. He says he came home the long way round. He asked me to give you his love."

I could not say anything. I did not want to cry, I just wanted to smile and smile, and when I looked round all the men were smiling at me too. Sister had to go back to her work, and I went back to my R.A.M.C. orderly. He shook my hand warmly. "That's a bit of good news, eh, Nurse? Real glad I am, an' the lads'll be too!"

The lads were wonderful; they shared in my happiness as if it were their own, increasing, if it was possible, the glorious sensation of relief and joy that filled me that evening. "I don't think we've ever had a nicer bunch of men in the block," I told Mary enthusiastically that night as we undressed. "I could have kissed them all with the greatest of pleasure." I pulled my dress over my head and threw it on my bed. "I think soldiers are heaven. I love 'em!"

She laughed. "If they could see you now in your pants and brassière they'd love you! Clare, you have got long legs. You ought to have been a dancer."

"I wanted to be once, when I was a kid. I think the parents had ideas about ballet too, but they turned it down."

"The life too tough for their cherished daughter?"

"Cherished daughter too tough for ballet. Father said I'd be too tall—and I am. I'm five eight. You can't be a ballet dancer at my height; you're too heavy. All my poor little partners would wilt if they had to pick me up." I spun round on one leg in my happiness. "Mary, isn't it heaven not to have to worry about one's nearest and dearest any more!"

She said mildly, "The War isn't exactly over yet, dear."

"Phooey! I agree with the men. It'll be much better now we're on our own, and not cluttered up with gormless allies." In my energy I knocked my dress to the floor. I picked it up, and as I did so something dropped out of the pocket. I recognized the little object as a parting gift I had received from one of our Frenchmen."

Mary held out a hand. "What's that?"

I gave her the brooch. "One of those Maginot Line badges."

She read aloud the arrogant engraving we knew by heart. "*Ils ne passerant pas.*" She grinned. "Not bloody likely." She passed it back to me. "What are you going to do with it?"

"Keep it for my grandchildren."

"My dear, they'll have had half a dozen fine wars of their own by then. They won't want to listen to your war stories."

"They certainly will—whether they like it or not. No point in living through a war if you can't bore people with your war stories afterwards. I'm going to be a fearfully tough grand-mother, and my grandchildren will say, 'Yes, Grandmamma, no, Grandmamma, anything you say, Grandmamma!' I promise you they will."

"To produce these grandchildren you'll need a husband first. What about that?"

I removed my remaining garments. "That can wait until after the War. If I have a husband I want to have him around, not just for a couple of days, and then at the end of a 'phone or as some nebulous writer of letters. I don't hold with war mar-riages." I wrapped my dressing-gown round me. "No stability. I want stability—a home—kids—the works—but not to a back-ground of war. Fun's fun, but a girl doesn't want to laugh all the time. So right now I'm going to spend at least an hour in a bath. Want me to run you one?"

I could not spend an hour in that bath, as Joe Slaney rang me while I was still in it. I went along to the telephone room, feeling damp and a little peeved at being denied my long soak.

Joe said he had called to tell me he was delighted Charles was safe. "Care to come over for a drink to celebrate? I could pick you up at once, if you like."

"You can't do that; I'm not dressed. I'm just out of a bath."

"Well, hell," he answered reasonably, "you can dress, can't you? Or are your feet too worn out?"

"Actually, they are." I thanked him for his call and invitation. "Joe, do you mind if I say no, honestly? I am thrilled about

Charles, and if I wasn't so whacked I'd love to celebrate. There's another point against going out; Sister said he was going to try and ring me later, and though I doubt that he'll get through, as our line is always out of order for trunks, there's faint hope that he might manage it, and I wouldn't want not to be here."

He said he quite understood. "You stay where you are; put your two feet up, and maybe have an early night."

He was being so nice that I felt slightly guilty about refusing to join him. "Sure you don't mind?"

"I'm breaking my heart," he retorted. "The damned organ is rattling inside me right now, in many little pieces. I'm in a shocking state—but I'll be worse before I'm done."

"Why not go to bed early yourself? You look as if you could use the sleep."

He laughed. "What's come over you, girl? Since when have you cared two damns about how I look?"

"Since you passed out at my feet. I have to keep an eye on you in case you do it again. You're bigger than I am, Joe. You might take me down with you next time."

"Well, now," he said, "it mightn't be a bad idea at that——" and he rang off.

I smiled at the receiver as I replaced it. I certainly had walked into that one. The telephone rang again while I was watching it. It was the office wanting to talk to Madam. I went to look for her, told her she was wanted, and went back to the bathroom for my things. Mary was in the bath I had vacated.

"What did Joe want?"

"To date me this evening. Drinks at the Mess."

She soaped her sponge and handed it to me. "Wash my back, Clare. What did you say?"

"Not to-night, Josephine!" And we both rocked with laughter at my feeble joke, because we were on that delightful plane of happiness where the most infantile remark strikes one as exquisitely funny.

Next morning we arrived on duty to find the hospital square littered with stretchers. The stretchers were covered with grey blankets, and occupied by men whose faces were the same colour as their blankets. They lay still, mostly with their eyes closed. They were not dead, yet they did not look like living men.

We stopped a sweating stretcher-bearer. "Where are these from?"

He wiped his brow with the back of his hand. "The Navy fished this lot up yesterday. On some hospital ship they were. Seems as they lost a couple of thousand in that lot. These are some of those Scots lads as went from here, and that Geordie unit what pulled out a month back." Four more ambulances crawled into the square as he was speaking; they stopped just inside the arch. They could not get closer to Casualty because of the stretchers. " 'Struth. Not another lot." Our informant shook his head. "I dunno where we're going to put 'em. Be shoving the lads up on the roof next, we will."

We walked on, threading our path in and out of the many stretchers. We smiled at the men on the ground—one or two smiled back, the others returned our smiles with staring eyes that seemed to see nothing.

We found Sister and Joe were already on duty. Sister had removed her shoulder cape, her sleeves were rolled high, her face hidden behind a white mask. Joe was improperly dressed in his shirt-sleeves, his stethoscope dangled from his neck, his face, like Sister's, was disguised by a mask. Beryl Jacks, tired, and rather fractious, told us that Sister and Joe had been on duty since half-past four that morning. "We've shifted all the men you left in here last night. An enormous convoy left for Garden East at six. God, what a night! I thought we had had the worst. Last night just took the biscuit."

Sister gave us a brisk report. "We've still got twenty empty beds, but they'll be filled in the next half-hour by the look of what's left to come in. None of our men are dangerously ill, some are seriously hurt, all are badly shocked. They were in the sea for a long time. Will you two give every man as much hot tea as you can get them to drink, and give them as many cigarettes as they want? There's a crate of cigarettes under the kitchen table. You needn't keep count. When you've done that start on washings and dressings, one at each end as before, and work towards the middle. If I finish my round with Mr Slaney I'll come and help you, but the round is bound to take a very long time, as we have not had a proper chance to look at them, and have only just got them into their beds. Leave the other admissions to me; Mr Slaney will see them as they come in, and help me get them into bed. Breakfasts are going to be sent over an hour later this morning, to give us a chance to get the men comfortable first. All right? Good."

Mary turned to go, then turned back. "Sister, what about breakfast? Shall we knock off when they come up, serve them, then go back to the washings again?"

"If you haven't got through by then, yes." Sister smiled faintly. "And, incidentally, if you get around to the cleaning and want the polish-tin, don't bother to look for it. It's empty. I lit the fire this morning. I agree with Dillon. Floor-polish is the only answer."

The cookhouse orderly arrived just then with buckets of fresh tea. "I'd take it in for you, ladies, but I haven't the time. Time! I tell ye! We've served one complete round of breakfasts, and now we've another to do."

73

Mary took one bucket from him. "Did you feed the men before they left us, Jarvis?"

"You won't do that for days. The poor devils have been stomachs?" he queried severely, and marched out as if he had the cares of the hospital on his shoulders.

The men drank their tea gratefully.

"Ta, ever so, Nurse. This is the stuff."

"Och, Nurse, this is real good tea. And we can have a wee smoke? Ye're spoiling us!"

I did not see Sister, Mary, or Joe for over an hour. Then Joe appeared at my elbow as I removed the large iron kettle from the fire and added boiling water to my bowl of washing-water. "All under control?" he asked.

"More or less, thanks. I haven't got through the first layer of oil on any man yet."

"You won't do that for days. The poor devils have been soaking in it."

"Were they really on a hospital ship that was sunk?"

He nodded grimly. "Red Crosses and all; she's now at the bottom of the Channel. She was a genuine hospital ship. Unmistakable. Must have made a good target. Finished with that kettle?"

"Yes, it's pretty empty. Want me to get you some more water?"

"I'll get it myself," he replied shortly. "I'm just about capable of doing that."

I followed him into the ward, and noticed that he was stooping this morning. I felt suddenly sorry for him—poor old Joe—he looked really depressed; I felt a pang of shame at being so content myself, yet it did seem such a good world. Why did men have to mess it up like this?

The Highlander I washed next was a long, dark man with a soft voice. I was sure his hair was black until I washed it with ether soap and discovered it was a flaming ginger. His body was so begrimed with oil and salt that it was only after I had changed the water in my bowl four times that areas of his skin showed signs of approaching cleanliness. I apologized to him for taking so long.

He smiled. "I am thinking it is I who should be apologizing to you, Nurse. You are being very gentle. Rub harder. You will not be hurting me."

"Have you no pain anywhere?" I scrubbed his chest. "Sure?"

"I am only sure that I am having a very pleasant wash and am very comfortable."

Beneath the oil and the dirt I discovered thirteen large flesh-wounds on his thighs and legs. The most severe was in his right

74

thigh. When I had washed off the filth it showed to be flayed from his hip to his knee. I washed on, very carefully, and under the still thick oil saw a glint of metal. I stopped what I was doing. "I'm afraid you've still got some shrapnel in there. Didn't you feel it?"

"Only a wee bit," was all he would allow. "It was paining me when I was walking."

I finished washing him, covered his worst injury with a clean towel, then laid a couple of blankets over him. "I'm going to leave you for a moment. I want to ask Sister about you."

Sister was in the next ward, helping Joe set up a blood-transfusion. I told her about the Highlander. She said simply, "Take it out, Dillon, and put on a flavine dressing. It can't stay in."

My patient was patiently smoking when I returned to him. He stubbed out his cigarette politely. I asked if he would mind my removing his shrapnel. "I'm afraid it may hurt a bit."

His blue eyes were untroubled. "If it will not be troubling you, Nurse, I will be very grateful for you to pull it out."

I set a sterile-dressing tray, left it on his locker, tightened the strings of my mask, scrubbed my hands in the sink in the nearest ablutions annexe, and went back to him with my hands held high as if in prayer. I felt like praying; I was very scared at the prospect before me. I had done dozens of simple dressings before, but nothing like this. I consoled myself with the thought that my Highlander must only be slightly injured in comparison with the badly wounded men in the Acute Blocks, and that if Sister had not considered this dressing easy she would not have told me to do it.

The initial stages of the dressing went well, as I was only removing oil, now with a swab held by forceps rather than a flannel in my hands. Then I took a pair of artery forceps, gripped the protruding end of the piece of metal in the forcep's teeth, and attempted to remove it gently. The shrapnel refused to shift; now I was gripping it I could feel how firmly it was embedded in the tissue of his thigh. I looked at him.

"I should have another cigarette. I'll wait while you light it."

I waited, watching his face. There were beads of sweat on his forehead and upper lip, mingling with the beads of oil that remained despite the many washings I had given his face. When his cigarette was drawing I said slowly, "I'm very afraid I'm going to have to hurt you a lot. Would you like to hang on to the bedrail? And do curse if it helps you. I won't mind at all."

He smiled slightly. "I will just be spitting teeth, Nurse. You do what has to be done. I will not be moving."

I tried twice more to shift the shrapnel gently with the forceps. Gentleness was no good. I wrapped my left hand in one of the towels from my tray and leant on his knee, took a much firmer grip on the forceps with my right hand, pulled carefully. The metal moved slightly, but refused to come out. "Hang on, Jock," I said, "I'll try and get it over quickly." I tugged really hard that time, the shrapnel shifted, and with a sickening slither came free. It was a piece of steel half an inch broad at its widest and nearly five inches long. When I had felt it give properly I also felt violently sick. More than sick—I felt light-headed; my vision was suddenly blurred. I thought wildly, God, I can't faint now! I turned away quickly with the metal, dropped it and the forceps in a kidney dish, and forced myself to look back at the wound. To my utter astonishment and relief it was only bleeding slightly. I looked at his face, and what I saw there helped me pull myself together. His colour was greenish, and he was now sweating so freely that his sweat was black with the oil it was forcing from the pores of his face.

"It's all over now," I said, dressing his wound rapidly. I took up the half-smoked cigarette he had dropped in his ash-tray and put it between his lips, holding it for him while he inhaled. "Poor boy. I'm so sorry I hurt you like that. I'll get you a cup of tea in a minute."

His lips were white. "Poor Nurse. I am thinking it was not a nice job for a young lady."

"I'm a nurse. This is what I'm here for."

He reached out and touched my apron skirt. "And I and the boys are thanking God that you are being one."

I badly wanted to cry. Instead I covered his leg with the blankets. "Thank you. It's nice of you to say that."

"It is not nice of me at all, Nurse," he contradicted in his gentle voice. "It is the truth I am speaking. It is good, when you have seen all the bad is being done, as we have seen, to know that there are people like you young ladies who nurse us who are doing only what is good. You cannot be knowing, Nurse," he added sincerely, "what it is meaning to all of us to come back and find you nurses waiting here to be kind to us. We are being very grateful to you."

At that I nearly broke down and wept over him. I did not want to embarrass him, so I rushed away for extra blankets, another hot-water bottle, tea, and brandy. I had to force the brandy on him; he wanted me to drink it instead. While he was sipping the tea I had to leave him in a hurry. I ran to the ablutions and vomited into the first latrine.

Someone came into the ablutions as I was vomiting. I felt a hand on my shoulder, and heard Joe's voice. "Now get your head down, girl. That's it. Down between your legs. You'd best

76

kneel on the floor as there's no chair. Good girl. You'll be better soon."

The floor was about to hit me in the face. It did not, because of that guiding hand. I raised my head once. Joe's face loomed disproportionately large and close to me. He wiped my mouth and forehead with some cloth, then squatted by me. He was still in his shirt-sleeves, and his shirt was spattered with bright blood. "All right, Clare?"

"Yes, thanks." My voice sounded odd, but as I could talk I decided I must be all right. I stood up unsteadily.

He caught my shoulders. "Relax. Just let yourself go limp for a moment. I won't let you fall. And I won't say one word about the blind leading the blind or this making us quits."

I was too giddy not to obey him. I let my head drop on to his shoulder and let him take my weight. As I stood there I heard a drum beating. I moved away. "What's the drum doing? Not another band, surely?"

"No band, no drum, no music. This isn't the day when everyone has to burst out singing. You were up against my heart. It must have been that you heard." He looked me over. "You're all right now. What made you vomit?"

I told him. "I hope I took it out correctly?"

"If the chap and the shrapnel are both intact, and he hasn't bled, you did it right. Five inches, did you say? I'll come back with you and take a look at him."

When we were clearing the lunches that day our Commandant appeared in the hall. She looked unusually concerned about something. She spoke first to Sister, who was at the desk with Joe. Sister did not look my way, but I saw the look Joe shot at me, and I saw him wince. I wondered what Madam could have said to have that effect on Joe. Then Miss Moreby-Aspin was at my elbow. "Dillon, m'dear, I want to talk to you. Sister says you may leave the ward and come with me to the office."

I glanced at Sister. She nodded. "It'll be all right, Dillon. Frantly-Gibbs will be able to manage the clearing on her own. Go with your Commandant."

Mary's eyebrows were raised to her hairline. I caught her eye and shrugged slightly, then went out of the Block with Madam.

She took me to her small office, closed the door, told me to sit down. She did not sit down herself, she leant against the edge of the desk directly in front of me. She did not say anything for perhaps a minute; she just looked at me, and breathed carefully as if she needed to conserve her breath. It was hot in the little room, the windows were closed, and the sun blazed through the glass turning the room into an over-heated conservatory. The scarlet potted geranium that ornamented the desk was wilting for lack of water, and the muffled throb of the ambulance engines outside in the square made the room sound as if it was filled with weary bees.

Miss Moreby-Aspin said very quietly, "Dillon, m'dear, I am afraid I have to give you sad news." And to my eternal gratitude, without wrapping the words in tactful cotton-wool, she told me at once that my father was dead. Then she explained how he had been killed.

5

A BIG BLACK CROSS

I COULD not believe her; I could not believe that the world could go on without my father. I had been braced against the news that Charles might die—Charles was so gentle and vulnerable; I had thought about Luke dying—you cannot have a brother at sea in a war without the thought occurring to darken your mind; it had never occurred to me to worry about my father. He was strong, middle-aged, a general practitioner in that small seaside town in Kent where I had grown up; he was indestructible, and he was my father. I had not forgotten his passion for sailing, I simply had not thought it important; he had said that his beloved yawl would have to be beached in our garden for the duration. I had never connected the *Margurita* with the War.

I sat and stared at her as she repeated the telephone conversation she had had earlier with my mother. "Your father and his partner were away for three days. Your mother said she understands they made several trips. She asked me to tell you that Uncle Michael is well, and that he was with your father when he died yesterday morning. Your mother knew nothing until your father's partner brought the yawl back late last night." She moved from the desk and stood with her back to me at one of the windows. "I don't have to tell you, m'dear, how distressed I am for you."

I said, "Thank you very much" as if she had passed me the salt. I sat still on that hard chair, and slowly I realized what she had told me, and I realized that I was never going to see my father again. I could not fully comprehend that; how could I be alive if he was dead? Yet I was alive, and she said he was dead. And the last time I had seen him was at a railway station. He had dropped me off on my last leave; he had not been able to wait for my train to come in, as he was late for surgery. He had kissed me quickly. "Take care of yourself, darling; write to your mother—she loves getting letters from you brats—and remember, if you want us, Mother and I are here at home." He had driven off swiftly; like all family doctors, he was always overworked, always in a hurry, never in for a meal on time, never far from his aged black bag. I did not wonder if he had taken his medical bag in the *Margurita*. I knew neither he nor Uncle Michael felt themselves dressed without their bags in their hands. I gazed at the potted geranium, and saw, not the slightly weary petals of that flower; I saw two greying, portly G.P.'s in their fifties lugging that wretched *Margurita* down our garden and on to the beach, shoving her off the pebbles into the sea. Two ordinary, middle-aged fathers, sailing to bring the men home.

Miss Moreby-Aspin had moved. She stood behind me and put an arm round my shoulder. "I have seen Matron; naturally, you may have compassionate leave. I have looked up the trains for you. You will have to go through London; the cross-country journey is out of the question at the moment. I would rather you did not leave this afternoon, as you will almost certainly be delayed several hours, miss your connexion in London to-night, and I do not like the idea of your having to spend to-night on your own in London. I think you should leave by the first train to-morrow morning. I will arrange transport for you. Do you agree, m'dear?"

"Yes. Thank you."

She patted my shoulder. "Right. I'll see to it. Now, about the rest of to-day. Would you like to be excused duty? Matron says you may do exactly as you choose."

I had no feelings, no wishes, no tears. I was quite numb, and very cold. "I'd rather not go off duty, Madam, but I don't mind what I do. I'll do what you say."

She helped me to my feet as if I were an invalid. "I'm going to take you to have some lunch. I know you don't want to eat, m'dear, but you're a sensible girl, and you'll eat. Then I want you to go back to your Block. You'll be better working. I'll send a wire to your mother for you. I'll try and book a trunk call for you, but you may not be able to get through. Your mother told me she had to wait four hours to talk to me."

No one mentioned my father when I returned to the Ob. Block after lunch, yet every movement they made when I was around made me aware of their unspoken sympathy. There was a great deal of work to do, and Sister made sure that I did it. She did not give me a spare second until she sent me off duty at six. She held out her hand as she dismissed me; "Dillon, I wish I could say something that would help, but I can't. Good-bye; good luck. I won't be here when you get back. I've been posted. Thanks for all you've done."

Joe was waiting by the cycle-rack. He had tied my cycle on the back of his car. "Get in, Clare. I'm going to run you home. Archie Oliver's standing in for me for an hour."

The trance-like stare in which I had existed since I followed Miss Moreby-Aspin into her office still held me in its grip. I obeyed him mechanically. He did not run me straight home. He stopped at his Mess. "Come in. You're going to have a drink." He took my arm and walked me into the hall, pushed me like a stuffed doll down on to a leather sofa, vanished for a few seconds, and returned with two glasses. "Ever drunk neat whisky before?"

"No."

He gave me the glass. "You're going to drink it now. Knock it back. It won't go to your head to-day." He sat down by me and produced cigarettes. He lit two together and handed me one. "I know you're in uniform. Forget it."

He said nothing at all after that. We sat there in silence for perhaps fifteen minutes. I was grateful, and faintly surprised by his sensitivity. He was equally silent in the car when we drove the rest of the way. Only when we arrived at the V.A.D. Mess did he speak. "When you get back, Clare, if you feel glum give me a ring. I'll buy you a drink. If I'm still here."

"Thanks, Joe. For that—and this. Why? Think you'll be posted? Like Sister?"

He nodded. "It's on the cards." He looked at me. His eyes were half closed, making two brilliant blue slits in his sallow face. "I'm sorry your father's dead, Clare. I'm very sorry. I wish I could have had more than one hour in which to help you now. I wish there was more time—for a lot of things. There isn't." He got out, walked round the car, and opened my door. "Hope the train doesn't get held up too many times for you to-morrow."

"Yes." I thanked him again. "See you when I get back."

He put his hands in his pockets. "I'll be around. Maybe." He stayed standing by his car while I walked up the steps into our home. I did not see him drive away.

Late that night I got out of bed and went out into the garden alone. It was a very quiet night. The moon was full; very bright, very low, it hung over the tennis-courts like a great white foolish balloon. No convoys of lorries heavy with dumb men roared along the road into the camp and disturbed the night; the air was broken by not one but three nightingales, singing in rivalry in three separate trees. I listened to the nightingales, and tried to think of our home without Father, without his humour, his solidly reassuring presence, and the gentleness of his hands. I wished I could weep; I could not. I lay and watched the moon, and thought how stupid and lonely it looked, and how stupid and lonely I must look, lying in this quiet garden on this lovely peaceful midsummer night. I fell asleep at last on that grass bank beyond the first tennis-court. When I awoke the sky was red with the new daylight; the birds were singing their dawn chorus, and the grass beneath my cloak was soaking with dew, as if the earth had wept my tears for me.

When I got back from my compassionate leave Miss Moreby-Aspin told me I had been moved from the Ob. Block. "I'm not sure if your transfer is temporary or not, Dillon, m'dear.

Matron's got her hands full, with all her Sisters being posted overseas and their places taken by the new Sisters called up; our members are just as bad. All my old girls are being moved, and now," she added sadly, as if this were the last straw, "the A.T.S. are to have a permanent hospital of their own. They've taken over a couple of those empty houses in the M.O.Q. for the purpose, and I've had to send Frantly-Gibbs down to live there. Carter and yourself must go along and help Frantly-Gibbs until our new members arrive. I'm expecting ten more in the next week. Carter will sleep down there, pro tem.; you'll have to stay in your room here and cycle down daily. Cut along at seven-thirty to-morrow morning and report to Frantly-Gibbs."

I cycled out of our Mess next morning with mixed feelings. I detested leaving my beloved Ob. Block and the men; I was not enthralled with the prospect of nursing A.T.S., pleasant young women though they were; but I was delighted to continue working with Mary. And if she was going to be boss until we had enough patients to rate a Sister life might be highly amusing.

I had gone about a quarter of a mile when a lorry overtook me, screamed violently to a stop, and a man jumped out of the front seat. It was Staff Williams.

"Hallo, Miss Dillon! Couldn't leave the camp without saying good-bye to you. I didn't know as you were back." He wrung my hand. "Missed you from the Ob. Block, I have. How you been keeping?"

"Well, thanks. Nice to see you, Staff." I looked meaningly at the new light paint on his tin hat. "What's that in aid of? Don't tell me you're leaving us?"

He grinned. "You might say as I've already gone, miss. On me way out, I am. This morning an' all."

"Staff! You mean you're deserting the Pack Store? You can't do that. How are we going to manage without you? How dare you go off to sunny climes and leave us with no one to guide us through all those forms?"

"You'll get by, miss." He wagged his head. "You know your way about now. Reckon I'd best be getting on." He shook my hand a second time. "All the best, miss. I—er—was real sorry to hear about your dad. Shame. Still, you'll keep your chin up. Your brother doing nicely?"

"Fine, thanks. He's at St Athan now; the other one is home on sick leave with his leg in plaster. How about your son?"

"He's beat his dad to it again. Went overseas last week, he did. Maybe I'll catch up with him. Oh, well, miss, mustn't keep you. Glad as you happened to be on the road to-day. Cheerio."

"Good-bye, Staff. Thank you for stopping. And thank you for all your help while you were in your store. We're going to miss you badly. I do hope you meet up with your son. Good luck."

He climbed back into his lorry, the driver started the engine, and Staff Williams leaned out and waved to me until the lorry was out of sight. I never saw him again. He was killed in Africa later that year. I often thought of him—of his rigid soldier's figure, rigid soldier's face, kindness, and incredible patience. Mary wrote to tell me he had been killed, and I wrote back:

"I can't believe it. I'm sure somewhere he's presiding over a celestial store handing out white wings and harps with a resigned expression. 'You young Angel ladies! What will you be wanting next? All right, take 'em—but that's me last pair of best whites, and me last set of halos, and how I'm going to make up me numbers I don't know. Never mind, miss. Don't you worry. I'll see to it for you.' Mary, I don't mean to blaspheme, but he did so love his store. He was one of your good men. I do hope he's happy."

An open ambulance stood outside the gate of one of M.O.Q. houses that morning. Mary and Agatha greeted me from the back of the ambulance. "Clare—nice to see you again! Come and join in."

Mary put down a tray loaded with medicine bottles and jumped down into the road beside me.

"How are you, dear?" she asked more quietly. "And your mother and the boys? All well?"

"Mother's been wonderful. Both the boys got home. Luke's still with her. He's on sick leave." I thanked her for the very sweet letter she had written me. "It was good of you to write."

She rested her hand on my arm. "It's nice to have you back with us. Now, shove your bike somewhere, come and help us shift these things in, and then we'll have a cuppa. We've got to empty this ambulance first, as Green is burning to get away."

Green was the R.A.S.C. driver of the ambulance. He overheard Mary's final remark. "Too Green to burn, miss!" He smiled delightedly at his own brilliance. "Where do you want me to put them bowls?"

"Put everything in the hall, please," said Mary. "We'll organize them later. Clare—take this tray for me, will you?"

Agatha came away from the depths of the ambulance in which she had been rummaging. She held up three urinals. "Why have they sent us bottles? There are about twenty here. I thought this was for A.T.S. only?"

Mary said placidly, "Well, dear, you never know; they may come in handy. We're meant to be only catering for A.T.S., but that doesn't mean we will. We may have to take an overflow of troops from the hospital, and if we do that we'll need bottles. Shove 'em in the hall."

Obediently we shoved everything in the hall of that first house, and incidentally blocked the foot of the stairs so we had to unstack into the garden, then restack all over again. Despite his expressed hurry, Green helped us willingly.

When the removals were over for the moment Agatha sat down on a pile of folded sheets. "Thank goodness that's done. My back's breaking. What about that cuppa, Mary? Think our union will allow it before we do any more?"

Mary said she thought our union would be all for it. "What about you, Green? You got time for some tea?"

Green said he reckoned it would be a black day, it would, when a lad couldn't make time for tea. "Much obliged, miss."

Mary smiled, and suddenly bellowed, "Sarge? Half-time?"

"Who's the Sarge?" I asked.

"Sergeant Stevens. Our A.T.S. cook. She's O.C. kitchen, and has a couple of Volunteers as minions. Merrick and Blakney. Nice kids, both. The Sarge," Agatha explained, "is a bit terrifying on sight, but she's all right underneath."

Sergeant Stevens was a youngish woman with a tight bun and thin lips. She was a good cook, and a better organizer. She popped her head round one of the doors leading into the small hall in answer to Mary's bellow. "Come and get it, ladies! It's all set!"

Green accompanied us into the kitchen and sat on the table with us three V.A.D.'s and the two A.T.S., while Sergeant Stevens poured tea from an enormous metal pot. "Sugar, all?"

The tea was very strong and very hot. Green was very content. "I hope as they want some more stores fetched along of you, Sarge. Bring 'em like a shot, I will. Best cup of char I've had this week, this is."

As we drank our tea Mary explained roughly what was to be our work. "We are to get both houses ready to take twenty-eight beds in each. We've got to spring-clean first, then organize as a hospital wing."

"How soon do we expect patients?" I asked.

Mary said no one had told her that. "As soon as more A.T.S. than can be dealt with in Families fall sick." She looked hopefully at Merrick and Blakney. "You girls feeling well? Wouldn't you like a few days in bed? We V.A.D.'s are going to get hellish bored once we've got the houses straight."

Merrick and Blakney giggled. "Give over, Nurse! What'll the Sarge say?"

They were pleasant girls, given to giggling, whom we discovered to be fantastically hard workers. Green whispered something to Merrick just then, and it produced such an outburst of giggles that both girls had to leave the room.

Sergeant Stevens refilled our cups. "You men!" She scowled at poor Green. "Carrying on that way with two girls! Shocking, I call it!" She glanced through the window, and her jaw dropped. "And there's the Sergeant-Major! And this place all in a mess—oh, dear—oh, dear!"

Agatha was looking through the window too. "It's only Monica Gilroy." She slipped off the table, went out to the hall, and came back at once with a very pretty fair girl in A.T.S. uniform. "Monica, this is Clare Dillon. Clare—meet Monica. We were at school together—and now she turns up as a Sar'nt-Major."

"Good Lord." I was too surprised to say anything else. I noticed Green was also staring open-mouthed. Monica was very pretty.

She laughed at my astonishment. "Have you never seen one before?"

"Not a female one."

It was too much for Green. He climbed off the table. "Reckon," he murmured, to no one in particular, "I'd best be getting off. Ta for the tea, Sarge. Morning, all."

Mary washed her cup. "Come on, girls. Let's leave these exalted lady soldiers to their kitchen. We've got to rub up our lamps and transform M.O.Q. 3 into a hospital. Thanks for the tea, Sarge. Give us a shout when you want us to eat again." Agatha and I followed her into the hall. She told us to help ourselves to buckets and scrubbing-brushes. "I hate to break it to you, Clare, but every floor in both houses needs scrubbing. They're filthy after standing empty for so many months."

Agatha said she quite enjoyed scrubbing floors. "I find it soothing—only I detest getting my apron messy. Think we dare take them off, Mary?"

"I don't see why not. No one can scrub a floor in a spotless apron, and keep it spotless, and do the job properly. If Madam turns up and makes a fuss we'll put our aprons on again. Quite simple."

We spent all the morning and most of the afternoon on our knees. When we finished the house smelt fairly pleasantly of wet, clean wood and our knees were sore. Mary said we could leave the other house until next day. "Let's shift that stuff from the hall. And let's be highly organized. Agatha, you do the stock cupboard, linen, and cleaning-things; Clare, you be O.C. bathrooms, turn them into sluices if you can; I'll put up beds all round, and we can make them up later."

Some time later Mary came into the second-floor bathroom to see how I was getting on. "How's it going, Clare?"

"Fine. Only one snag; we've so much equipment that when I get it all in one no one'll be able to open the door."

She sat down on one of the fracture boards I had put across the bath. "Somewhat different from the Ob. Block."

"I'll say. Couldn't we have done with all these glass trolleys

85

there! Look at them; we've got six on each floor, and we had only one for the whole Ob. Block! And all these lovely, lovely instruments—and that dirty great electric sterilizer that is sitting outside this door on the floor! If they had these things in store—why couldn't they have let us have them there?"

"God knows." She yawned. "That scrubbing's just about finished me." She looked round the crowded bathroom distastefully. "Oh, how I'd like to be back in the Ob. Block! I've always detested housework, and I don't like this having no patients."

I said I'd been hankering for the Ob. Block all day. "I feel frightfully cut off after one day here. We haven't heard one single rumour to-day. The invasion might have started, and they've forgotten to tell us."

"You'd better ring up Joe Slaney. He always has the latest."

"Is he still here? When I left he thought he was about to be posted."

"He was here two days ago—and, what do you know—he's got a third pip." She smiled wearily. "I was rather pleased. I got very fond of Joe during that rush. I must say he surprised me. I never thought he'd turn into a proper doctor before my very eyes, but he did. He worked like a black—and looked like death. But I suppose he must be all right, or he wouldn't have got another pip. He's shifted from the Ob. Block too. He's now M.O. i/c Acute Surgical. There's a new boy in the Ob. Block. Serious youth called Peters who never drinks anything but coffee."

"That'll make life tricky there. At least Joe was happy with the dregs. What's happened to Thanet? Where did she go?"

"Hospital ship. Don't know which one or where, except it was obviously foreign parts, as she had to get tropical kit. She went three days after you, and some dear old girl—the old Mother Smith type—was hauled out of some small hospital and shoved into Reserve uniform. I quite liked what I saw of her. Fat, untidy, but jolly kind to the men. Joe said he thought she was a pretty fine nurse of the old type." She laughed suddenly. "She clucked over the men and called them 'son' and told them to be 'good boys and do this or that.' They loved it. I think she reminded them of their mums."

Sergeant Stevens pushed open the bathroom door as far as it would go, which was not far. "Well, I never! You have got a crush in here! Come along, Nurses, tea's growing cold. It's nearly six."

We were still making the beds when we noticed it was growing dark. I looked at the curtainless windows. "What do we use for black-outs?"

Mary went downstairs to investigate, and returned with a

load of Army blankets. "Sarge says these." She made a face. "And do they smell!"

Agatha sniffed the blankets. "Horse." She beamed at us. "I say, girls, maybe we're going to take troops after all. That's why they've sent us horse blankets."

Mary dropped them intentionally on the floor. "Think these'll make the troopers feel less homesick, now they're mechanized?" She experimented with one blanket against the window, tucking it along the empty curtain rail. It promptly fell down.

I picked it up. "Whatever the reason, our nice clean rooms are going to smell like stables." My casual remark christened the A.T.S. hospital. For as long as it remained in use, the place was known as "The Stables"; the name became so well known that later many people thought it had been the original name of the first house.

Next day we scrubbed and organized the second house. Miss Moreby-Aspin arrived while we were having more belated tea. Mary offered her a cup. "No, thanks, Frantly-Gibbs, m'dear; haven't the time. There's a war on, m'dear. I've just come to check your surgical stores for Matron, and to tell you that three new members have been posted here. They'll arrive at the end of the week. Put them into that room next to yours and Carter's."

Mary protested, "It's pretty tiny, Madam. It only just takes two beds as it is."

Miss Moreby-Aspin slapped Mary's shoulder heartily. "Don't fret about little things like that, Frantly-Gibbs, m'dear! The new members will have to get used to roughing it!" Agatha, Mary, and I held our breaths expectantly, and to our great joy Madam boomed, "They've come to take men's places. They've got to expect to live hard, like men."

Mary went off to check the stores with Madam, and Sergeant Stevens promptly turned on her subordinates. "Hear that, you two? And you thinking that the nurses have a soft life! Soft! They know what work is if anyone does!"

The Sarge gave us V.A.D.'s a vast amount of pleasure. We invented a third sex for her benefit: men, women, and nurses. She obviously no more considered us women than our Commandant did; women joined the A.T.S., men the Army. She tolerated us kindly, and scolded us when necessary. Mostly she humoured us, and held the firm theory—which made it sad to remember that she had never worked with Joe—that no member of the medical or nursing profession can exist for more than half an hour without being refreshed by a large cup of tea.

Once the Stables were clean and ready for patients the enforced holiday that followed irritated the three of us. We wandered round the empty beds like lost souls and even Mary was put out. "If we don't have any patients soon," she said one evening, as we rolled sufficient cotton-wool balls to plug the wounds of a division, "I'll go out with a machine-gun and bring 'em in that way. This sitting here with nothing to do is giving me the willies."

Agatha said she was so bored she could scream. "Sarge was narking about her back this morning. I did my best to persuade her she might have anything from a damaged spine to renal trouble, and ought to come into one of our beds, but she wasn't having any. She said she'd do nicely with a couple of aspirins, thank you kindly, Nurse, and would I like a cup of tea?"

"Tea!" I groaned. "Ugh. I'm awash to the back teeth with the stuff."

Mary smiled faintly. "Just as well you never took to Joe Slaney, dear. If you had you might have spent the rest of your life drinking tea."

"Which, if I had no other reason, would stop my marrying him."

Agatha was intrigued. "What's all this? Did Joe Slaney have a yen for Clare?"

"Anything but," I told her. "He and I were like red rags to a bull to each other. Until the big flap started when everyone buried hatchets all over the place. And he was," I had to add, "very decent about Father. He really was sweet that evening."

Mary said we were all very young and stupid and she was very old and wise. "Joe Slaney always gave you the old green light, Clare. I noticed it dozens of times in the Ob. Block."

"Then why did he never do anything about it? He and I have been around the same camp for months."

"Didn't he try to date you a couple of times?"

"Once because we were having a fight and, being an Irishman, he couldn't resist the pleasure of going on fighting. The other was just an odd gesture when he was bored. You can scarcely call the ardent passion."

Agatha said she thought Joe could probably be madly ardent. "The Irish always are. Joe always looks pale and haggard and far-far-awayish, as if he's planning a private war of his own. And he has the most fascinating eyes in the camp! Really, Clare, it's too bad of you!"

"What have I done wrong now?" I asked in surprise.

"You've let Joe Slaney get away!" She seemed genuinely annoyed. "Monstrous waste of a good man."

"I wouldn't call Joe that. A good waste of time, maybe; a splendid tea-drinker. But I am sick of tea."

Mary gave me my second surprise in a few seconds by saying calmly, "I think Agatha's right, Clare. I think Joe is a good man. I've alway thought it a pity that you held him off the way you did."

"I didn't hold him off. I didn't do anything. There was never any need to repel boarders when Joe was about. He made no attempt to board."

Mary and Agatha exchanged resigned glances. "Clare," said Agatha, "hasn't anyone ever told you that unless a girl shows willing no normal man ever makes a pass?"

"Nurses!" Blakney, pink and breathless, burst into the room. "Sarge said to tell you to come and see quick! Come out front and see what's coming in!" She leant against the lintel of the door and sighed ecstatically. "Ever such lovely boys! Thousands of 'em! All with ever such queer hats! Sarge says as they must be Aussies!"

"Wow!" Agatha leapt from her chair, scattering cotton-wool balls all over the floor, and raced after Blakney out of that back room, across the hall to the front door. Mary and I followed rapidly, ignoring the snowfall of swabs around us. Our arrival in the garden was greeted by a magnificent cheer from the men, who marched in a leisurely fashion along the road in front of the line of houses. The cheer left us unabashed after our months in the camp; we smiled and waved at the men. Mary, leaning on the front gate, called, "Are you Australians?"

"Too right, Sister!" they roared back. "The Aussies are here now to help the Old Country, and that's dinkum! The War'll soon be over now, girls. Good to see you!"

As the next contingent drew level with our gate the young officer marching with his company saluted; the N.C.O.'s and the men copied him. Agatha said shakily, "I think I want to cry."

I glanced at Mary. Large, unchecked tears were rolling down her cheeks; I knew my own face was wet. I could not have explained why I was weeping. I was only aware that the sight of those ranks of young men with fair, tanned faces, easily swinging arms, their casual self-confidence and air of supreme gaiety, touched me beyond expression.

Two days later I was sent back to the Ob. Block and found it already occupied by members of the A.I.F., who appeared to suffer from N.D.K.'s and P.U.O.'s quite as frequently as did our own Army.

We loved all those tough Australian fighters; their advent as patients lightened the hospital. They were so gay, so delighted to be in hospital, and consequently among women again; so uniformly correct in their attitude to us. "Our dads told us to treat you gals real good, sport. What do you say, Sister? Will you marry me?"

Proposing marriage was their favourite pastime. I collected four proposals in my first week back in the Block, and was feeling very pleased about my new-found sex-appeal, when

Sister, who was twice my age at least, confided that she had had seven. "The dear naughty boys! I can remember nursing their fathers when I was your age, my dear. We did have fun with them. There was no knowing the pranks they'd get up to!"

Our new patients taught us a great deal in a short time. They taught us all the words of *Waltzing Matilda*; that Sydney Harbour was worth looking at, that the fall of France was 'a fair cow,' that 'bloody' is an Australian term of endearment; how to play 'two-up' directly the M.O.'s round was over; how to laugh when you least felt like laughing; and how the only possible way in which to keep an Anzac in his bed, if he was not dying, was to remove his blues and pyjama trousers.

I was very pleased to be back in the Block, but I missed Mary badly, and although Mrs Yates was a kind woman and a good nurse, I missed Miss Thanet's streamlined efficiency, and the fact that, as we belonged to the same generation, we had the same sense of humour. What surprised me most about my return was how I missed Joe. I saw him occasionally in the square; once he stopped to say he was glad I was back, and must drop into the Ob. Block some time for a cup of tea. If he did drop in it was when I was off-duty. I never saw him in our Block again, and I could not avoid a certain wry amusement in contrasting his real attitude towards me with the ideas expressed by Mary and Agatha. I decided to cycle along to the Stables on my next half-day to tell the girls how mistaken they had been, and how lucky they were to have left the main hospital, and been spared working more than a few days with our new M.O., Mr Peters. Mr Peters was a serious young man who suffered from acne and an inflated ego. He clearly considered V.A.D.'s were lowly creatures who existed only to open doors for him or serve him coffee. He reprimanded me sternly about the latter. "Do you call this stuff coffee? It's far too weak—and you must have left out the salt!"

I dwelt lovingly on Joe's habit of drinking tea-dregs as I answered. "I'm so sorry. Coffee-making is not one of my virtues —or duties. I think in future you had better make it yourself. Failing that, you're welcome to the men's tea. Captain Slaney found that quite satisfactory."

When my half-day arrived Sister gave me the morning instead of the afternoon free. Kirsty Forbes, the girl who now occupied Mary's bed in the Drawing-room, was also free that day, and we lay in luxury watching our colleagues get up early.

Kirsty had only been with us for two weeks, and this was her first half-day. She sat up and stretched her arms. "This is sheer heaven, Clare. Do we often get mornings off?"

"If your home is too far to reach in an evening, yes; the afternoon halves are saved for girls who live near."

She said she was delighted she lived in Scotland. "I'll get us both a cup of tea. That's allowed, isn't it?"

"Oh, yes. You can help yourself to breakfast, and bring it back if you like. Madam's very good about things like that."

She climbed slowly out of bed, strolled over to one of the open french windows, and stood sunning herself. She wore a grey chiffon nightdress that was transparent as a summer cloud. She had a beautiful body, and looked quite lovely.

The morning air was as usual filled with the noise of aeroplane engines; Spits from the fighter station that had replaced the Training School at Upper Weigh; an occasional bomber returning off-course to the bomber station thirty miles west. Kirsty, being still new, watched the sky curiously. "I say, Clare," she called mildly a few seconds later, "what does a 'plane with big black crosses on it mean? There's one coming awfully low, and it must have a silencer on it or something, as it's not making any noise. It's going to come down in the garden if it isn't careful."

I had already bounced out of bed. I hurled her body away from the window just as she finished speaking. "It's a Jerry, you idiot!" We fell together behind one of the beds and began to laugh. We were still on the floor and still laughing when we heard the crash. We stopped laughing, and went back to the window. We could see what was left of that German bomber quite clearly. It had missed the tennis-court and crashed into the open field on the other side of the road. There was a new encampment at the far end of that large field; the men poured out of their tents like brown ants from an ant-hill; then, like us, they stood poised, watching. As we watched the petrol tanks suddenly exploded and the wrecked 'plane was hidden behind a white sheet of flame.

I sat down on the bed nearest the window. Kirsty remained standing. "That might have been a close thing!" she announced cheerfully. She looked round. "I say—you've gone green. No need to panic now. Nothing's happened."

I looked at the white flame. "There must be men in that."

"A few Jerries less," she retorted simply. "What do you care?"

I said, "They may have wives—girl friends—and they're burning to death in front of us."

She came and sat by me. "Now look here, Clare," she said reasonably, as if I were a difficult child, "we're supposed to be fighting a war. Those are our enemies. Get that? If you hadn't pulled me away from the window they'd have thought nothing of knocking me off for a lark. You've got to think of things that way. You'll go bats if you don't."

"No, I won't. And I think that after you've been here a little while you'll think like I do." She shook her head. "You will," I insisted, "I'm certain. You can't stay dispassionate and stay a nurse. You'll find people are people—and they matter—no matter what language they talk. You'll find you can't help thinking of them as not soldiers but men—ordinary men—with wives and kids—and you won't be able to help wondering what those wives and kids will feel when they hear about something like this. It isn't only the sight of men being turned into lumps of charcoal that makes me feel sick—although God knows that's sickening enough! It's the thought of their families—parents—and the hell it'll be for them to-morrow or the day after, when they hear about this." I retched suddenly, remembered Joe's advice, and put my head between my knees. I kept it there for a while. When I sat up Kirsty was staring at me as if I was quite mad.

"You really mustn't work yourself up like this over half a dozen dead Jerries, Clare. Take a grip. I'll go for that tea."

She returned with the tea, wearing a patient expression to show she was going to humour me because I could not take it. She was right; I could not take it then, and never could. It often struck me that I spent three-quarters of my nursing life holding patients' heads while they vomited or wept, and the remaining quarter doing both those things in some ablutions annexe or sluice-room myself.

I met Joe as I went on duty at one. He said he had been talking to Kirsty. "She says you saved her life to-day?"

"Moot point. Those Jerries were too busy for target practice."

He tapped his leg with his cane. He was becoming much smarter these days; at times he really looked like a soldier. "She said those chaps bought it at the bottom of your garden."

"Not quite. In the field opposite."

"We heard the crash from here." He looked at me keenly. "You saw it happen."

"Once it was down."

"How did you feel about it?"

"Sick."

He nodded. "I know. Gets one in the stomach. Poor bastards. One thing—it must have been damned quick for them." He looked up at the sky. "Where's the sun gone? It was a grand morning."

"The sun's on my side. It knows I've got to work all afternoon, so it's hidden itself tactfully behind those clouds. Looks rather like rain." I sniffed the air. "Doesn't smell like rain. I wish it would rain. I'm sick of fine weather."

"Selfish young woman, aren't you! It's my half-day. First I've had for ages. I was hoping to get out of camp for once. I've a drop of petrol, and thought I'd get myself a pass and some fresh air. After spending the last week in the theatre, solid, I need air that's not tainted with anæsthetic. And I'm sick of the sick and the War. I want to go and look at some birds."

"Do you like looking at birds?" I was interested. "Charles was nuts on bird-watching when we were growing up. He used to drag me along with him and make me disguise myself as a bush."

"Hell of a skinny bush you must have been. Yes, I like it. And why wouldn't I, being the only son of my old man?"

"Your father a bird-watcher?" My brain gave an almost audible click. "Are you that Slaney? Or rather, the son of that Slaney? The *Survey of British Birds*?"

He smiled. "You're not going to tell me you're educated, Clare? What would you know of my old man's book?"

"Only that it nearly broke me, because I gave it to Charles for his seventeenth birthday."

"Did you now?" He seemed very pleased, and I was very pleased to see his obvious pride in his father's work. "This is quite something. I was beginning to give up. I was afraid we had nothing in common. What time are you off to-night?"

"Eight. Why?"

"Why not have dinner with me? We can have a grand time talking birds. I can pick you up here when you come off, and if I can raise a pass for you too we can go out of camp. There's quite a good eating-spot just before Upper Weigh. The R.A.F. generally have it booked solid, but I may be able to ring them up and reserve a table. If not we could take a chance. What do you say?"

"I'd like it very much. Thank you. I'd love to get out of the camp. I've got claustrophobia coming on fast."

"Well, now, you've got yourself a date." He tucked his cane under his arm. "Now, no standing me up for an Australian. Run along to your jolly afternoon with the soldiery, and spare a thought for me and the long, peaceful afternoon I'm going to have off from the big war. And when they ask me, 'And what did you do in the Big War, Daddy?' I'll say, 'Son, I watched birds.'"

He had barely said that when an anti-aircraft gun barked sharply; a second gun opened up directly after the first; and instantly the camp air-raid sirens began to wail in warning.

Joe looked up at the low grey sky. "Why, oh, why," he asked sadly, "could I not have kept my big mouth shut?"

"It might just be practice."

Another gun cracked. Joe raised one eyebrow. "If it is someone's wasting one hell of a lot of the tax-payer's money. Hear that, Clare?" He tilted his head to listen. "That's no far-off thunder, dear. For my money it's pal Jerry come to have a look-see. I've a hunch our little friend Kirsty is now going to see quite a few nice pretty aeroplanes with lovely big black crosses on them. We'll have to beat it, Clare. You to the Ob. Block and me to my damned theatre."

THE hospital siren screamed like an agonized banshee as I crossed the square; the ambulances scurried under cover; the sick men in wheel-chairs on the Block balconies and in beds on the flat roof over the entrance arch were hastily wheeled and lifted inside the wards by their attendant Sisters and V.A.D.'s. In the Ob. Block Mrs Yates wore her tin hat on top of her large, flowing Army cap. "I refuse to remove my veil," she said firmly. "I have never appeared in a ward incorrectly attired, and no German is going to make me do so this afternoon." Yet she insisted that we V.A.D.'s in her charge should remove our own caps. "Fix the straps of your tin helmets securely, Nurses; you don't want them dropping off and crowning a wounded man when you bend over a stretcher. You should by rights have your respirators at the alert"—I noticed her respirator lay on her desk—"but the wretched things do get in the way so when you're working. Keep them handy, and slip them on if you see the P.A.D. officer or the C.O. coming this way."

The bed-patients were highly amused. "Got to put me tin hat on, have I, Nurse? What? An' me in me nightshirt? Cor, strike a light! Proper carry-on this is—still—if you say so, Nurse. Ta, That do you?"

The up-patients, forbidden the ramp, crowded round the ward windows until Sister shooed them away as if they were a set of mischievous schoolboys. "Call yourselves fighting-men? You ought to be ashamed of yourselves! Do you not know better than to stick your silly noses to a pane of glass when a bomb is liable to go off? If you've nothing better to do help the nurses pull all those beds away from the wall. That's right." Sister looked round at what we were doing. "Get all the bed-patients in the centre, Nurses, then put the mattresses from the empty beds against the windows to prevent any glass coming in."

Mr Peters strolled in looking consciously casual. He wore his tin hat almost on the bridge of his nose, and his respirator was strapped firmly at the alert. "You look as if you're expecting trouble, Sister. Have you forgotten the large red crosses we have painted on our roof?"

Sister turned on him. She was a plump, homely body, but she looked very dignified at that moment. "I have not forgotten, Mr Peters. I have not forgotten what happened in the last war, either. I spent three years in various hospitals in France. I know very well with what respect the Germans treated our red crosses then, and from what I have heard they have not altered."

The men who had been in France this time nodded at each other. "Aye," they murmured, "she's right, that old Sister."

Five minutes later Mrs Yates and those men were proved right. From the sound the raiding aeroplanes appeared to be directly over the hospital; there were no guns in the hospital grounds, but the hospital was right in the centre of that great camp, and every gun in the camp seemed to be firing in our furious defence.

The men grinned appreciatively. "This'll learn Jerry to take pot-shots at hospitals! Hear that ack-ack, Nurses? (As if it was possible not to hear.) Must have around five hundred ack-ack guns going on this camp! Cor! Hear that? That's another opening up!"

The noise was overwhelming, and strangely exhilarating. The men who had been in France were triumphant. "Jerry's catching it good and proper this time! We got something to hit back with here—and the lads are hitting back real good!"

Suddenly we heard a whistle. It was a soft sound against the greater noise of the guns, but all the experienced soldiers reacted instantly. "Down flat on the floor, Nurses——" and to ensure we did as they said they pulled us down with them. I found myself under a bed when the bomb exploded; when I sat up I saw most of the mattresses had been blown from the windows by the blast. The windows were shattered; miraculously, it seemed to us, outward.

Sister brushed down her skirt. "We will put one mattress over each of the bed-patients." She walked calmly through the Block, instructing us. "Now, you boys in bed, I want you to be good and stay under those extra mattresses. You won't stifle, and they'll make a deal of difference if the roof falls in. Just be good lads. There." She might, by her manner, have been tucking down a nursery for the night. "Now, you three nurses. It seems——" She had to stop and duck in mid-sentence. When we were on our feet again she straightened her tin hat, rearranged her veil, and continued. "It seems this is going to be bad. We will split up. Each V.A.D. to one ward. I will take two; Mr Peters, you will please take two. We cannot risk all being killed together. It would cause great inconvenience to the office."

She sent me back to the first ward. The soldier who had pushed me under the bed apologized for knocking me down. "When you hears the whistle, Nurse, you don't stop to ask questions. You wants to get down flat and cover your head if there's cover."

No more bombs fell close to the Block that afternoon; the

noise lessened, faded, died away. When the all-clear sounded we were all in high spirits, triumphant at being alive and unhurt, delighted to see through our broken windows that the hospital appeared untouched, and enthusiastic about the strength of the camp's anti-aircraft barrage. Jerry, the men said, had found he wasn't knocking over a row of skittles this time, he wasn't!

Our high spirits were short-lived. Not all the camp was untouched, and before our beds were back against the walls, or the mattresses replaced on their rightful beds, the first casualties began to arrive. Our telephone rang immediately. Sister answered it. She came into the first ward. "Mr Peters. Will you go to Casualty at once?"

It rang again as Mr Peters, looking rather pale, was leaving the Block. Again Sister answered it; again she came back to the ward. "Miss Dillon, will you go to the Acute Surgical Block? They need more nurses. Stay there for the rest of the day."

I collected my cloak before I left in case it was colder tomorrow. It was just as well I collected it. I never returned to work in the Ob. Block again.

The A.S. Block consisted of five twelve-bedded wards and the operating theatre. It was always staffed by three Sisters, and six V.A.D.'s. The men in that Block were sick men, most of whom were newly post-operative. The men who came in that afternoon were even more sick, and to make room for them we had first to remove the patients from their beds. There were no orderlies to lift the patients on to stretchers, or to carry the stretchers down the iron staircase to one of the convalescent surgical blocks, since all the orderlies were either busy in the theatre or—the vast majority—had gone out with the ambulances to help bring back the injured men. But the chaplains were there when we reached the Block—not only the three hospital chaplains, but others from the camp who had come up spontaneously, removed their jackets, rolled up their shirt-sleeves, and seized one end of a stretcher.

When I reported to Miss Mason, the Sister in charge, and Senior Sister in the hospital, she told me to go and help with the moving. "We must have the beds empty, Miss Dillon. I've got fifteen men lying on my duty-room floor at this moment. Go and lend a hand where you can."

I joined Kirsty and Father O'Brien, the R.C. padre. "Shall I carry your end for you, Forbes? You know more about what's going on than I do."

"Thanks. I've got to get these beds made up clean."

Father O'Brien was a short, tubby little man with a strong brogue. He said he would hold the stretcher steady while I helped the sick man on to it. "And if ye can tell me of a finer way to lose my fat, son, I'll be glad to know it! Right, boy, the

96

Nurse'll be lifting ye're legs on; there, that's it fine! Now ye put ye arm round her neck and she'll manage. That's the way, Nurse. I see ye have the touch. Now if ye'll be taking the feet I'll take the head. Off we go."

I had never lifted a stretcher before; from that afternoon I acquired a new respect for the men who carry those heavy, unmanageable objects. Going down the iron staircase was one of the nastiest experiences of my life. I was terrified that I was going to drop the ends; terrified that the patient would slip off; terrified that poor Father O'Brien, who was sweating heavily, was going to fall on top of us. Somehow we reached the bottom safely, walked the few yards necessary to the ward in the block below, and put down the stretcher. My hands shook badly when I let go. Father O'Brien smiled at me. "It's heavy work for a woman. You managed well, child. We'll go back for more."

As we carried back our empty stretcher I asked, "Father, why can't we use the lift?"

"They've had to keep it for the boys going up. They're in a bad way. They couldn't stand the stairs—not even on a stretcher."

When we reached the A.S. balcony one of the other sisters came up to us quickly. "Father O'Brien, you're needed in the end ward right away." She nodded at me. "Go and find Mr Gill, the C. of E. padre. Ask him to go to the duty-room at once." She looked at my face, and recognized I was a stranger from another block. "Are you here permanently or just up from the convalescent block?"

"For the afternoon, Sister. I'm from the Ob. Block."

"Thank God for that. Go to the end ward yourself. They want every pair of hands they can get in there."

There were twelve beds in the end ward and twelve stretchers on the floor by the beds. Both the beds and the stretchers were occupied by men who had been wounded in the afternoon's raid. A blood-transfusion stand stood between every bed and stretcher; there were twin bottles of plasma on the stand, twin rubber tubes going down, one to the bed, one to the stretcher. The Assistant Matron was working there; she told me to go and find as many hot-water bottles as I could, fill them, bring them back. "Fast as you can, Nurse."

I tucked one of those water-bottles under the feet of the soldier beside whom Father O'Brien was praying. He looked up, still on his knees, and saw what I was doing. "Give that bottle to another boy, Nurse," he said very quietly, "it will not be wanted here." And as he spoke he covered the face of the soldier whom I had supposed was unconscious. "The poor lad has passed on; God rest his soul."

"You, Nurse." The Senior Sister was by me. "Go and get me

three more dressing-drums from the theatre. And on your way look in at the duty-room and see if Mr Gill is there. Tell him he's needed in here now." She turned to the chaplain. "Father, that boy in the corner is asking for you."

The warning light that showed an operation was in progress was on over the theatre door. I found the sterilizing room open, went in, and helped myself to three dressing-drums. A voice called, "What do you think you're doing, Nurse?"

I turned to see a masked and gowned figure behind me. She sounded like a Sister. "Miss Mason asked me to fetch these, Sister."

"I see. Well, next time, remember to ask permission. All right, take them. Don't help yourself again."

I apologized and raced back to the ward. I found the dead soldier had been moved; a new man was in his bed. Sister sent me for blankets, brandy, tea, more hot-water bottles, more blankets, more tea. Then she took me to one side. "Go and sit by that boy in the corner bed and hold his hand. There is nothing more we can now do for him. He's frightened. Stay with him. If anyone tells you to do anything else say I told you to stay by him."

The soldier in the corner bed had a sterile towel covering the left half of his face. The towel was fixed round his forehead and neck with two large bandage bows. The bows seemed to me indecently large and frivolous; I was still too inexperienced to realize they were tied that way intentionally, as a large bow was easier and quicker to untie than a small one.

He blinked at me with his free right eye, as if he found difficulty in focusing. His eye was bloodshot, the skin around it purple with contused blood. He said, "Hallo, Nurse."

"Hallo, soldier." I touched his hand and smiled at him, hoping that smile would cover the fact that I was very scared, as successfully as the sterile towel on his face was covering what injuries lay underneath. "How are you feeling?" The touch of his fingers made me want to jump away. His hand was ice-cold; his fingers moved stiffly, like a skeleton hand, as he gripped me. "What's your name?"

"Raines." His voice sounded peculiar. There was no depth in it, no tone. His accent was educated, and when he spoke again it was as if he was imitating the absurd, rattling voice of a character in a film cartoon. "Raines, J. S., 6429271; 'B' Company, Royal——"

I stopped him. "I don't want to bother you with your number and regiment. Just your name. What's the J. S. stand for?"

"John Stephen." He closed that one eye. "The chaps call me Johnny."

"John's nice; so's Johnny." I could not think what else to say, or what to do. My hand was growing cold in his. I had to say something. "My name's Dillon. Clare Dillon." I knew we were not meant to tell the men our Christian names; I did not know how we were meant to talk to the men while they died. No one had ever told me that. It was not in our training manual, either.

He sighed heavily. "Clare. I knew a girl called Clare. She was a friend of my sister's—she——" His voice trailed off slowly like a gramophone record running down. "She was fat and she had spots. She was—quite—good—fun—though"—he sighed again—"and I don't suppose—she could—help—having—spots."

"No. I'm sure she couldn't. Lots of people have spots." I was growing desperate. Surely there was something I could do for him? There must be more I could do than just hold his hand. "Would you like a drink?"

"No, thank you. I'm not thirsty." He screwed his eye, opened it once more. "I'm frightfully comfortable. I just feel sort of vague. But I wish"—he stopped for a vast breath that did not seem to do him any good—"I wish I could see you—properly. I—can't. You're all blurred—and—they—said I had to keep this other eye covered."

"It doesn't hurt you? Sure?"

"Nothing—hurts—any more. It did—but they gave me something. I feel much better now I've had it." The exposed sibe of his face twisted horribly, and at first I thought he was in pain, then I realized he was smiling. "I was a bit scared, you know. I—I thought—I'd bought—it. But I feel—much better now. Silly, really. One always panics."

"Yes. One does." It was an effort to keep my expression under control. I looked round the ward, and found my own vision momentarily blurred. It was like looking at a forest of dead, white, leafless branches, and on the branches were scarlet and yellow fruit. I blinked, and saw the bare trees were transfusion stands; the fruit was the vacolitres of blood and plasma. The floor was thick with stretchers; the beds heaped with still bundles of grey; as I watched, two men in shirt-sleeves lifted one of the grey bundles from the bed and lowered it on to the floor. I saw a Sister hastily sweep all the clothes off the bed, throw on a clean mackintosh and under-blanket and stand back, while two other men lifted another figure on to the bed. I recognized one of the men as Joe. I did not recognize his expression or the brisk manner in which he moved as he helped his colleagues carry a dead soldier from the ward.

John Stephen Raines was talking again. "Nurse, could you just shift this dressing affair a bit? It's awfully uncomfortable. It keeps tickling my nose."

His voice sounded much stronger; less rattly. I felt cheered, warmed. "Of course. Tell me if I hurt you."

"I'm sure you won't. I can't feel anything."

"Good." I smiled as I bent over him and untied the bows. "You've got a couple of highly classy bows here—I hope I can tie them——" and then my own voice ran down as I saw what lay underneath that large linen towel. "As well," I had to add, as he was expecting it.

There was nothing that you could recognize as half of a face under that towel, very little that you could recognize as half of his head. It was as if someone had taken a knife and cut away everything from the side of his nose to an inch or so behind where his ear must have been. He was watching me, so I had to keep a fixed smile on my face. I hoped his blurred vision would prevent his seeing the smile could not touch my eyes. My hands shook badly as I retied the bows. "Better? Afraid I haven't made as good a job of the bows as Sister."

He said, "It doesn't tickle any more. Thanks. Tell me," he panted slightly, "have I got a whacking black eye?"

"Yes." I had to be careful with my own breathing. "Yes. You have."

"It doesn't hurt," he raised his other hand slowly to the towel, "but I can feel it's—sort—of—puffing."

I caught his hand. "You mustn't touch the dressing, John. You—er—might dirty it."

"I forgot that." He did not take his hand away from mine. "Of course, you have to be—fearfully careful about—sepsis—and what have you—don't you?"

"Yes. That's right." I did not dare look at the towel now; I did not need to look at it to remember what lay beneath; I did not think I would ever be able to forget what I had just seen.

For some time—it might only have been a few minutes, it might have been an hour, I could not tell—he was semi-comatose. Occasionally he asked about his friends. If many of them had been hurt? If I had nursed them? He asked about Father O'Brien. "Nice little chap. Good of him to come in to see me. He was fearfully quick. Did he happen to be in the hospital?"

"Yes, he was here."

"Is it padres' visiting afternoon or something?" Now he seemed to have forgotten the raid.

"Something like that. The chaplains are generally around when they're wanted. You're a Roman Catholic?" I knew he was, but I wanted to know if he had had the Final Rites of his Church administered. I had had no chance to ask any of the Sisters, but I knew from things my father had told me how very important this would be for him. "Would you like to talk to Father O'Brien again?"

"Don't bother him. He may be busy with some other chap. He was fearfully kind. He—er—said he thought it would be as well if—er—he did—all he could do for me. I was a bit scared then of—er—pegging out. Seems silly now. Wish I hadn't bothered him. I feel—fine."

"Good." His hands were growing colder, if that was possible. "Would you like another blanket?"

"It is a bit chilly—thanks."

I heaped three more blankets on him, and refilled his hot-water bottles. He grew no warmer, but a little drowsy. "I feel," he whispered weakly, "as if—I could sleep for weeks." Then suddenly, in a much louder voice, he said, "Nurse—I feel queer. Oh—Nurse"—he threw his whole body forward—"hold on to me—hold on to me—please!"

He was sitting upright now, swaying dangerously. I sat on the side of his bed and caught his shoulders, then slipped one arm round his waist, and with my other hand rested his head against my shoulder. His head flopped into the nape of my neck, like a weary child's. "I'll hold you, John—I'll hold you. I won't let you go—I promise I won't. You'll be all right in a moment—I'm sure you will." I spoke instinctively; I did not stop to worry what I should say or do, I knew exactly what to do. I stroked the uninjured back of his head gently, as my mother used to stroke our heads when we were children. "There, there. There's nothing to be frightened about. I'll hold you."

He did not answer. He gave a small, contented sigh as if that inexplicable moment of terror had passed, and to my infinite relief I felt his muscles relax as he leant against me.

Miss Mason came over to his bed swiftly. She must have been keeping an eye on him to have arrived by me so soon. "Has the pain come on again, poor lad?" she murmured, bending over my shoulder to look at the exposed part of his face. I could not see any of his face, as his injured left side was towards me. She touched his head, raising it from my neck slightly. Very quietly she said, "Lay him back again, Nurse." She helped me to do this, then covered his whole face with the top grey blanket. She looked over his body to me. "You did not tell him about his face?"

"No, Sister." My mouth felt dry.

"Good. I'm glad he was spared that. I am glad you were able to remain with him. The poor lad." She looked down. "One can only be grateful he did not linger." She straightened her back. "Go and wash your hands well, Nurse, then come back to me. And wash your face and neck, too. You have blood on both."

Blood. The air of the hospital was heavy with the sweet, sour smell; there was blood on my hands if not on my face, many times more that afternoon and evening. Later that night, and next day, when we carried the bloody-stained kit of the men who had died to the Pack Store, the sickly scent clung to our hands again, and remained to haunt the back of our throats for days.

One afternoon during the next week Mary cycled up from the Stables and called into the Drawing-room to see if I was off duty. Kirsty and I were sitting on the step of one of the french windows, writing letters.

Mary sat down beside us. "I hear you're now permanently in the A.S. Block, Clare. Like it?"

"Yes. There's a terrific amount of work to do, but it's sheer joy having masses of equipment. The Sisters are decent, too. Mason's a bit of a battleaxe at times, but she's a jolly good nurse, and teaches us a packet."

"Have you recovered from the raid in there? We heard that A.S. bore the brunt of that."

"More or less. Most of them died, so now we're about back to normal."

She looked sober. "We heard the death-rate was high."

"It was." We told her how high.

She winced. "How did you manage to lay them all out? That's not a thing you can hurry. Last Offices take ages."

Kirsty had become very much less academic about life in the last week. She said, "We didn't have time to lay anyone out. We only had time to roll them in blankets when they died, and then someone came and took them away. There wasn't time to ask where. We needed the beds too badly."

Joe rang me up three evenings later. "Clare, I'm on my way round. I'm not going to make a date. I daren't tempt Providence any more. I'm just going to drive your way, and if you're outside the house I'll slow down and pick you up. Try and be outside. I want to talk to you, and there mayn't be an opportunity after to-night. I'm on the move."

"Oh, Joe, not you overseas, too!" I rested my head on the wall above the telephone. "The whole world's going overseas. Charles already. Luke as soon as his leg's right for certain, he says. Thanet, Staff Williams, Mary's husband—now you. It's too much."

I heard him laugh. "Poor Clare. And to think I never knew you cared! Why don't you apply for foreign parts yourself?"

"Can't. I'm under age." I felt very depressed suddenly. I had got so used to having Joe around the hospital. If he went it would be as if the last of my great friends had gone. I had not realized until that moment that I counted Joe even as a friend. Apparently I did, and much good it was going to do me to count him as that now he was leaving. I said I would take a walk in the evening air. "I agree about no dates. Remember that dinner you asked me to?"

"I hadn't forgotten. Did you get any dinner that night?"

"No. Did you?"

"I did not. So what? It's good for our figures, if not our morales. And, Clare——"

"Yes?"

"Thanks for bracketing me with Charles, Luke, Staff Williams, Thanet, and Mary's husband. That was big of you. I'm now off to look for my rotor-arm, and then maybe I can get my car started."

"Have you got enough petrol?"

"Hell, yes. I'll use what's left in the tank. I'll not be needing it after to-day. I can't take it with me. I'm going to leave her in the Mess for anyone who wants her."

Ten minutes after that conversation I strolled out of the front door and down our drive. Joe drove up almost at once. "Surprise, surprise—now who would have thought I'd run into you?" He opened the door. "Hop in, Clare, and let's get out of this damned camp."

"What about passes? You got one? I haven't."

He said to hell with passes. "You got your Red Cross identity card? I've the usual. We'll take a chance. We'll probably be shot as parachutists, but what do we care?"

We drove along the main road out of the camp. We discovered there were road blocks roughly every thousand yards. We were stopped three times by Military Policemen, nine times by Local Defence Volunteers, but at none of the blocks were we delayed long. We were merely asked to show our identity cards, torches were flashed in our faces, and into the back of his small car, and then we were allowed to carry on.

"If Jerry overlooks these young searchlights they're all flashing around so happily," said Joe, as we left one barricade, "he's a bigger mug than I think he is. Do you think we can get any peace at all on this road, Clare? I want to talk to you, and I can't with these chaps playing soldiers all over the show." He looked round at the quiet countryside. "Do you suppose we could get out and walk round for a while?"

"If we do we'll almost certainly be shot at. They're all out looking for parachutists disguised as nuns, and I've got a cloak on and a white cap. Some lunatic might mistake me for a nun—particularly as I'm tall. We'd better stay in the car."

"Oh, my God." He slowed to a stop. "Another block. Let's have your card, Clare. And to think we came out to get away from it all!"

When we were a few hundred yards past that block he slowed and stopped the car by the side of the road. "Let's see if we can get away with it here. Those last chaps know who we are. And I must talk to you." He took out his cigarettes. "Have one."

As he lit my cigarette a Redcap corporal on a motor-cycle

drew up beside the car and flashed a torch in our faces. "Excuse me, sir, can I see your identity card, please?"

"'Struth!" muttered Joe, handing over both our cards.

"Thank you, sir." The corporal's manner was polite, but he flashed his torch up and down Joe, then me, and then looked searchingly through the car. "Were you and the lady planning to stop here long, sir? I wouldn't advise it."

I heard Joe sigh. I decided it might be a man's world and a man's war, but this was one of the occasions when the womanly touch might be successful. I leant across Joe. "Corporal," I begged, "the Captain realizes we ought to keep moving, but I did so want to talk to him, and he is posted to-morrow. This"—I managed to make my voice crack—"may be our last opportunity for a long time. Don't you think we could just stop for a few minutes? We won't get out." I felt Joe kick me encouragingly, and added, "Please, couldn't we just this once?"

The corporal returned our cards, tucked his torch under his arm, and drew on his gloves. "Sorry to have troubled you, miss. Beg pardon, sir. I'll see as you don't get troubled no more for the next half-hour. I'll just get the number of your car, sir." He walked round to the front, flashed his torch again, then was back by us. "Good night, sir—miss." He saluted, stepped back to his motor-cycle. and kicked it to life.

We watched his microscopic rear-light vanish. Joe began to laugh. "Clare, you devil! You almost had the poor chap in tears. I'm close to a manly weep myself. Where did you learn to lie like that?"

"I wasn't lying! Except about saying I wanted to talk to you, and not vice versa. That's just splitting hairs. Now," I sat sideways to look at him properly, "we've got half an hour by courtesy of the Military Police. What do you want to talk to me about?"

He coughed, turning his head sharply away from me as he did so. He had coughed several times during this interrupted drive. "Forgive me—smoking too much."

"You ought to give it up then," I replied absently, wondering just what he did want to talk to me about. With most young men of my acquaintance, I would have been quite certain that his desire to stop the car was merely to allow his hands to be free for a necking party. I knew perfectly well that that was the construction the M.P. corporal had put on our request to be allowed to remain in a parked car; but that M.P. corporal did not know Joe Slaney as well as I did—and that was not well by any means. However, I was tolerably used to young men on the verge of making passes, and, despite what Mary and Agatha had said about a girl having to show willing, I was convinced that Joe was not about to make a pass. He had never shown the slightest desire to touch me, and he was not showing it now. He was sitting in his corner, sideways, after that slight coughing bout, as I was sitting in mine. He was also sitting in silence, looking at me. "Joe," I reminded him, "get on with it. We haven't all that much time."

"We've enough," he said slowly. " 'Nothing is ours except time.' Even if it's only half an hour. It's ours."

" 'Nothing is ours'—who said that, Joe? Churchill? It's so dead right, it must have been him."

He gave a shout of laughter. "Darling, and I thought you were educated! The chap who said that was a little before the old man's time. Just a little. A chap called Lucius Annæus Seneca wrote it in a letter to a pal of his. You'll find it in his *Epistulæ ad Lucilium,* if you ever read Latin."

"I don't. But I have heard of Seneca—even if I can't quote him. My father may have—I mean, he may have had it. He had a lot of Latin books. I'll look when I'm next home."

"You do that. Tell me"—his voice was very gentle—"about your father, Clare. How do you feel now? Damn bad, still, is it?"

"Pretty bad." It was odd how easy it was to talk to him about my father. I had not been able to mention him to anyone—not even to Charles. "Not so much in the day, as we're so busy. But at night sometimes I dream he's still alive, then I wake up. And he's not."

He nodded. "It's the devil when you wake up, isn't it? How about your mother? And the practice? What's happened?"

"Uncle Michael's carrying on alone—and half killing himself with work. He managed to get a locum for a little while. Locums are hard to get now."

"What about the money angle? Has that hit your mother?"

"Inevitably, quite a bit, but it's not as bad as it might have been, as Mother has always had a little money of her own, and Father wouldn't let her use it, so it accumulated, and means she's got enough to live on. Just. The boys are helping. Of course, if it wasn't for the War she could sell our house, but who wants to buy a house on the south-east coast with all the invasion talk that's going on? It's not worth a couple of hundred."

"So she's hanging on to it? That's a bit of worry as well for you and your brothers."

"Yes." I explained how we had tried to persuade my mother to go inland. "We've some cousins in Buckinghamshire. She won't go. She says she doesn't want to let the garden get out of hand, and there's a lot of work she can do—mobile canteening—things like that. The place was stiff with troops when I was last home. Mother rushes up on the cliffs with her van and urns and serves them hot drinks on the gun-sites. She's been wonderful—and she says she's not going to give herself time to think—she must have work to do. Goodness knows, there's enough for her to do," I went on, "and it is just about the only thing when you're worried or upset. I think I would have gone up the wall about Father if I hadn't had so much to keep my mind occupied here."

"That's true." He lit another cigarette, and coughed violently. "Sorry, Clare—maybe I should give it up."

"You ought to do something about that cough, certainly. Where did you pick it up? I don't remember you having a smoker's cough in the Ob. Block. Perhaps you've got a chill."

"Let it be." He sounded bored with the subject of his cough. "The African sun'll clear it."

"That where you're going?"

"For my money—yes. I've to buy myself tropical kit, so where else? Every one's making tracks for Africa."

I said I could understand about that. "If we're going to be invaded won't we need an army here?"

"I wouldn't know. No one tells me anything." He stubbed out his cigarette, and played with the steering-wheel. "But there's something I want to tell you, Clare, and, as it looks as if I may not have the chance to tell you some other time, I'll have to tell you now. I have to tell you"—he twisted the wheel, and gazed ahead as if he was driving—"that I love you very much. I always have, and I think I always will." He spoke quite casually, as if he were discussing the weather. He dropped his hands from the wheel, and put them in his pockets. "I realize that I'm talking clean out of turn; I realize that this is really the first occasion that we've been alone together on a friendly basis. I'm not counting that evening you heard your father was dead. You weren't conscious what was going on that night. And before we've been fighting it out. Probably if I had any sense I'd have gone off leaving us fighting it out. I wouldn't have opened my big mouth about loving you, when you and I are still at square one. But I don't know when, or if, we'll reach square two. And since I have to leave you, I feel I'd like you to know what I feel about leaving you. I feel"—his voice was suddenly urgent—"like hell. I never knew anything could be such hell. And there you have it, Clare. For the record. Or to give you a good laugh. It's all yours with my love. And so am I."

I was not merely surprised; I was dumbfounded. "Joe—I don't know what to say—I never guessed."

"And why in hell would you? With me always beefing at you about playing hockey, and casting your eyes down? Anything for a bloody good crack—that's Slaney. Just call me Laughing Boy and have done."

"I won't call you that. And I won't have a good laugh. But for your record, thanks, Joe. Thank you——"

"Don't be such a prim little Victorian miss!" He turned on me furiously. "You don't have to thank the gentleman for proposing. I haven't proposed. I'm not that conceited! You've nothing to thank me for!"

"Oh, yes, I have!" I was equally indignant. "You were awfully kind to me that night about Father. You were marvellous. And I was grateful—and still am."

He grinned. "So there! Eh?" and we were both laughing when he went on; "Skip it, Clare. I'm glad if I helped you; I wanted to help you; I think I'll always want to do that, and if I ever can I hope I will. I didn't expect to fall in love with someone like you. Damn it, girl, you're as near as dark as I am! I've always gone in for blondes, not leggy brunettes—and then I walked into the damn Ob. Block one morning and saw you—and that was the end of the search for me. And what gets me is that I did not even know I was searching. I knew." His voice altered, his tone was deeper than I had ever heard it. "I knew. When I saw you. And as the odds are against our meeting again, I thought I'd tell you when I told you good-bye. Which is what I'm doing now."

He started the car without another word; he did not speak to me again, or attempt to touch me as we drove home, stopping at all the barricades. When we reached the house he got out to open the door for me. Only then did he offer me his hand, formally. "Take care of yourself," he said, as every one said in parting that summer, "see you some time, I hope. I'll be writing. Cheers."

"Cheers," I echoed automatically. "All the best, Joe. And get something for that cough. Some cough-mixture or something."

"I'll do that." He saluted me for the only time in our friendship, and waited by the car while I went into the house.

7

EXIT JOE SLANEY

I WAS too shattered by Joe's announcement to be able to sleep that night. Next morning I was off duty from ten to one. I rode direct from the hospital to the Stables. I had to see Mary. When I arrived the Stables nursing staff were in the kitchen being offered tea and hot buns by Sergeant Stevens.

"Hallo, Sarge, still at it?" I climbed on to the kitchen table. "Morning, girls. Nice to see how the other half lives. We don't even rate a tea-break in A.S. No time. How are the sick A.T.S.?"

Mary moved over to make room for me and said the sick A.T.S. were revoltingly healthy. "We can't keep the girls in bed. The moment our backs are turned they're up cleaning, bed-making, doing everything for themselves. They're even worse than the men in the Ob. Block! They know how to take temperatures and how to chart. I promise you, Clare, we live a life of idle luxury. Agatha's thinking of remustering."

"Remustering to what?" I wanted to know. "If you join any of the women's Services you'll have to be a nursing orderly or sick-bay attendant. Might as well stay in a hospital as do that."

Agatha said she proposed to stay in hospital. "A proper hospital, Clare. I'm bored with getting no place fast. It looks as if this war's going to be a longish one—I mean, we can't beat Jerry over-night, seeing as we've left all our bits and pieces over in France. I've decided to train. I," she announced smugly, "am going to be a nurse. The Real McCoy. An S.R.N. one of these fine days, and then I'll come back here in a super scarlet and grey uniform and lead you all a ghastly life in one of the blocks."

Mary shuddered. "It's a grim thought."

I said I didn't think Agatha would be such a bad Sister. "I wouldn't mind working under you, Agatha."

Mary said she had not been considering that angle. "I was thinking about the War lasting four years. It takes four years to become an S.R.N., doesn't it?"

"In the voluntary hospitals," replied Agatha. "I believe at Matthew and Mark's you take the State exam at the end of your third year, but have to work another as part of the contract because, although the State considers you are fully trained, the hospital doesn't, and won't give you a final certificate until you've done four years."

I was interested in all this. Momentarily it pushed Joe from my mind. "Are you going to Matthew and Mark's, Agatha?"

"If my interview with the Matron there is all right. I've got Madam's permission and her blessing. She said she thought I was showing the stuff I was made of, Carter, m'dear, and if she had been twenty years younger she would have come and trained with me! Now, girls, wouldn't that have been something?"

"Enough to make you stick as a V.A.D. for the rest of your life, dear," said Mary. "Have some more tea, Clare. You've only had one cup."

"Thanks." I held out my saucerless cup, reflecting on the advice Joe had once thrust at me. "I can't get over you leaving us, Agatha. When did all this come about? And why Matthew and Mark's?"

Agatha said she had been brooding on it secretly for some time. "I've been here eight months, Clare. And where," she demanded dramatically, "have I got? I'm still on the bottom rung, labelled Stooge, and likely to remain so labelled for the duration. I'm sick of stooging. I want to get somewhere."

"You'll be a stooge while you're training," I warned her. "My father was a Matthew and Mark's man, and he used to tell Mother and me of the ghastly time the pros had. Rules everywhere. And fearful Sisters. But it is a good hospital. Father said it was the only hospital."

"Thanet said that," put in Mary. "She trained there. Didn't you know that, Clare?"

"Did she now? I didn't know that." This made me even more thoughtful. "She was awfully efficient, and human at the same time. Mason's efficient as anything in A.S., but she's only human when someone's dying. If you turn into a Thanet, Agatha, you won't do badly at all. I must say, I think you're very enterprising. Going to be a terrific plunge starting all over again from scratch."

Agatha said she was scared stiff at the prospect, but intended going through with her plans if she was accepted. "One's got to get on in life, Clare. I don't know why, one just has. It's different for Mary"—she nodded indulgently at Mary as she spoke—"she's got a home and husband to go back to when all this is over. I haven't got either, and I'm the right age to train, and I like nursing, so, I feel, why waste any more time? All right, girls, laugh your heads off! I may be talking like Madam, but I am so sick of sitting on my bottom rung with never a chance of promotion. Take Monica. She started as a Vol. in the A.T.S. when I joined the Red Cross. She's shot right up the N.C.O. ladder and has just gone to an O.C.T.U., or whatever they call the courses for A.T.S. officers—and where am I? Still a miserable Grade One V.A.D., and having progressed to that, which I did after three months like you two, I can go no further."

One of the new V.A.D.'s whose name I did not know, said gloomily, "You were lucky, Carter. It takes us much longer now to even reach Grade One."

"My dear," said Agatha patronizingly, "what can you expect? We girls are pre-Narvik, pre-Dunkirk, pre-everything. We are the genuine old brigade. They had to give us something extra to boost our morales."

Mary slid off the table. "We'd better go and search for some work. If anyone is lost make some more swabs. The hospital can always use our surplus."

I followed them out. "Can I come and make swabs with you, Mary?"

She smiled. "Why? Haven't you got enough work in the A.S. Block? That I cannot believe."

"Not that. I want to talk to you, and I suppose as you're boss you can hardly knock off for half an hour mid-morning for a natter. So can we natter over swabs?"

"Better than that. Come into the office. I've a few notes I must write for Madam. I can spend quite a long time on the notes if I really want to. There truthfully isn't a thing to do for our ten highly co-operative patients. None of them are ill with anything more serious than minor sore throats." She led the way into her little office and closed the door behind me. "What's on your mind, Clare?"

I told her. "Mary," I said, when I had finished, "I was never so shaken in my life. Can you imagine Joe Slaney saying that to me?"

She said placidly that she could imagine it very well. "I told you I saw him give you the green light whenever you were about. He was never able to take his eye off you."

I shook my head. "I don't get it. Why wait until the last minute to tell me? Why didn't he do something about it before?"

"Would it have been any good if he had?"

"Well—I could at least have said no."

"Why should he ask for a rebuff? It was obvious you weren't interested. Joe's no fool, dear. Anything but. He's right on the ball. No man likes being turned down, you know. Men go in for pride, dear. Very much more than women do. No sensible woman really cares two hoots about her pride where essentials are involved. Men do. Then, few man are sensible in the practical sort of way women are sensible. He didn't propose?"

"He made quite a point of not proposing. He said—quote—he wasn't that conceited."

"He's too intelligent to be conceited. And a proposal of

marriage, although a tremendous compliment to the girl, also implies a certain conceit, since it takes for granted the fact that the proposer is the kind of person with whom some girl would want to spend the rest of her life. That's a big order, when you work it out."

"I had not thought of it like that."

"I should give it a little thought, dear. Joe, too. He's nice. What are you going to do about him?"

I looked at her. "I don't know. Nothing. What can I do? I don't even know where he's gone."

"He said he'd write. He'll let you know. Will you write back? Do you want to write back?"

I hesitated. "I suppose I do. I'm not sure. I'm all muddled. I don't like being muddled. It makes life too complicated. It was much simpler when Joe just irritated me."

"Forgive my sounding like Madam, dear, but life is a complicated business. I can see that you're muddled. I suspect Joe must have seen it, too. I think it was very nice of him not to propose."

"Nice of him?"

"Yes." She considered me thoughtfully. "He knows you've been lit up with a series of emotions lately. First, worrying about Charles, then the shock of your father's being killed, then the general set-up that's had us all up in the air, plus that air-raid. You're very young, Clare, and the very young can get very uncertain, when life proves to be strictly for adults only. As it is, all you kids are growing up fast, much too fast. And you must all be feeling, consciously or unconsciously, the need for the sort of security you should have at your age and aren't getting. That, fundamentally, I should say, is why Agatha's decided to train seriously. She's going to get security in the job. It's only right that she should want something to look forward to, and not exist—as we're all existing—in the very indefinite present. Have you realized," she added, "that we have all stopped looking forward to anything—leaves, dates, anything beyond to-day, or even now? Have you got a date for to-night?"

"No. Why?"

"If you had"—she shot at me with the suddenness of that last question—"would you be counting the hours until it came?"

"Of course not." I smiled. "Much good that would do! I had a dinner date with Joe the night of that raid. Taught me a sharp lesson if nothing else did about the folly of looking forward to something a few hours off. The War, or work, is bound to break it up. Always does. But what's all this got to do with Joe being nice?"

"That's my whole point. Joe sensed how up in the air you still are, possibly because he's up in the air himself. He isn't very

111

much older than you, and, like you, his whole life must have been turned upside down since this time last year. I know that what is happening to you both is happening to everyone of your immediate generation the length and breadth of the country; but the fact that the condition is general does not make it any easier for a specific individual. Living in the present is all right for children, to whom a day seems a lifetime, or to the very old. They've had a past, and can dispense with a future. Even people like David and I don't do so badly. We have stopped looking forward—but we can look back, if only to a handful of adult years. You kids can't. Consequently, it's only too understandable if you do rush headlong into uniform, marriage, or bed, in an attempt to grasp something tangible out of the intangible present. I should say that Joe Slaney used a considerable amount of self-control last night. I'm not suggesting he would have been able to pull you into bed with him, dear, but I am suggesting that had he played up the fire and the passion he might have persuaded you into becoming engaged to him." She smiled slightly. "I see you are shaking your head, dear, but remember you are shaking it in the cold light of day this morning. Last night you might well have been carried away by the darkness around Joe's car and the darkness ahead. Saying good-bye to even a casual friend who may well be on his way to be killed isn't easy. Saying good-bye to an attractive young man who just told you he loves you can weaken the strongest mind. If that good-bye is embroidered with a heartbroken offer of marriage any girl might well accept, because she hasn't the heart to send anyone off to possible death with a refusal. You're a kind-hearted soul, Clare. Joe knows that. He's worked with you. He is also as persuasive as an Irishman can be, when he wants to be. I should say he wanted to be that with you—very, very much. I'm glad that he wasn't. You aren't in love with him, and you'd have been horrified when you woke this morning and realized what you'd done. But as far as Joe's concerned, I do hand it to him. I think he behaved like that lamentably rare creature—a little gentleman."

"But, Mary—I would never have accepted him. As you've just said—I'm not in love with him. I like him—now. I like him a lot. I'm really sorry he's gone. But as for marrying him—the idea would never occur to me."

She said, "Did the idea that he was in love with you occur to you this time yesterday?"

"Of course not!"

She smiled. "Amazing how situations can alter in twenty-four hours, isn't it? And you don't have to be so up-stage about marrying him. Apart from the fact you might do a lot worse—you might well marry someone you've only known twenty-four

112

hours. It's happening all the time at the moment. I don't say it's a sound scheme at all; I merely point out that it does happen, frequently. And I'll tell you something, Clare, which you may not like. I think if Joe had turned on the pressure he could have got you to agree to marry him. I think he might even know it himself."

"Are you telling me," I asked indignantly, "that my subconscious is in love with him, and longing for me to fall into his arms with glad cries?"

"No. I'm merely reminding you that recently your subconscious has taken a series of beatings. One by one all the bulwarks around your private life have tumbled down. I don't only mean the obvious and greatest loss, your father; I'm thinking of your brothers, and your friends from home who are all scattered by this folly, your mother driving around in her van, half your house shut, and that whole house standing in one of the most dangerous spots in the country, so you can scarcely think of your home as a refuge any more. You may convince yourself you do not need a refuge, Clare; you may believe you can stand alone on your own feet. I don't doubt that you can do that if you have to; but I do say that if you were my daughter I would very much rather you didn't have to. Everyone needs some person or place as a refuge—and right now you have neither."

I said slowly, "There's my mother."

She looked at me. "I remember your telling me that your mother was gentle and quiet like Charles. Be honest, Clare; who lends the shoulder? Don't you feel your mother has enough to carry now she's on her own and has her constant anxiety for her two sons?"

I nodded. "I do. But how did you guess that?"

"It wasn't hard, dear. You and I know each other pretty well. I've only had to listen to what you've said. Also, I know how it is with my own mother. She's a perfect dear—a perfect Edwardian—she was sheltered as a girl—married long before the other war—and has remained sheltered. All our mothers are Edwardians and clean out of touch. One can't blame them; they behave as they were taught to behave by their mammas, who were Victorians. That speaks for itself. I'm quite sure your mother always taught you to behave like a little lady, and is quite sanguine about your being a V.A.D., because nursing in wartime is considered a lady-like occupation—by people who have never nursed in wartime. If your mother realized exactly what you've been doing lately, if she could have seen the work kids like you and Kirsty had to do after that raid, she'd have had a fit. You can't run to her and tell her how you felt when that boy with half a face died in your arms? Can you?"

"No. I couldn't tell anyone at home. It would only worry Mother and her friends. It wouldn't be any good telling them. They just wouldn't believe that sort of thing. I don't know what they think we do. Roll bandages, I suppose, and lay cool hands on fevered brows." I shuddered suddenly at the memory of John Stephen Raines' face. "I couldn't possibly say anything about that boy. Or"—I shuddered again—"Albert."

"Which one was Albert? The boy whose head was sliced across?"

"No. I didn't know his name. He died that first afternoon. Albert had no face at all, but he was terribly strong. He wouldn't keep any dressing on. He tore off whatever we put on, so eventually we had to leave his face exposed. He lived for two days, fighting mad and screaming. Mary, his screams were awful. Nothing seemed to touch his pain. Sister said it was probably because he was so strong and healthy. She said big men often do die hard. He did."

"Poor boy." Her face was lined with compassion. "Poor the rest of you. It must have been grim. I did hear about him from our M.O., but I did not know his name, or that he lasted so long." She fiddled with her pen. "Albert gave your subconscious another beating. You can't have a defence against things like that. Not until you've had the experience that Mason has had. Maybe after twenty years' nursing sights and screams do roll over your head; or maybe you just become a better actress. I don't know about that. I only know that in your first year of nursing you cannot remain untouched." She gazed at me in silence for a few seconds. "Listen, dear, I'm going to give you some advice. Don't take it amiss, and do think on it. To return to what I was saying, your defences are down, and when a girl's defences are down it is not very difficult to persuade her into anything. Take my tip, Clare, walk a little warily in the immediate future. I think you may miss Joe far more than you imagine. I think you are going to want something or someone to fill at least one of the gaps. The hospital is stiff with men who'll be only too willing. Don't get swept off your feet by X, because you avoided being swept off your feet by Joe Slaney."

"Mary." I sat down on her desk. "I'm not Agatha. I don't have to hold the young men off. Apart from the daft Australians, no man's made a proper or improper proposal to me since I've been in the camp. And don't mind me reminding you that we're surrounded by soldiers and not ravening wolves."

"Well, dear," she replied placidly, "I know you've been lucky so far, but some people do say those two words are synonymous."

I smiled faintly. "Perhaps it's just as well I lack sex-appeal. Not one wolf have I ever met here! no one's ever made an improper pass, much less forced me to run screaming from a fate worse than death. It seems I'm just not the type."

She thought this over. "Certainly David always said there was only one real weapon for a girl among men, and that is genuine innocence. He used to be very scathing about young women who allowed themselves to get taken for moonlight walks in the wood, and then got peeved by the consequences. I'm beginning to believe he's right. All the same, watch your step, Clare. As I've already said, you kids are all growing up much too quickly."

When I returned to our Mess for lunch Miss Moreby-Aspin sent for me. "Dillon, m'dear, I've got news for you. You're to come off day duty in the A.S. Block at twelve to-morrow and go on night duty. Pack your kit to-day and shift it down to the night house to-morrow afternoon."

I asked if she knew where I was going to work on night duty. When she told me I could hardly wait to leave her and ring up Mary. I did this before lunch. "Relax, my love. No more cause for anxiety from Aunty Mary. I'm leaving the wolves for the lambs to-morrow. I'm on nights in Families from then on."

She said softly, "Don't they have M.O.'s in Families, dear?"

I laughed. "Have a heart, Mary! Only that horrid little Peters and old Major Scott. Major Scott's a sweetie, but he must be at least forty-five. He's got grey hair. And he's married with five kids."

"Being married doesn't automatically remove a man from the list of wolves, dear. In fact, they often make the best." Then she also laughed. "I'll relax. I know I don't have to worry about Martin Scott, and I know what you think of the boy Peters! I'm really quite relieved to have you buried among the women and children. I've not been at all happy at the thought of you in the main blocks, without Joe or myself to keep a weather eye on you. Let me know how you get on, and give my love to Joe when you write."

"I don't know his address yet. I can't write until he does—if he does."

"He will. Remember I said he was a good man? Am I not being proved right? Always consult the Oracle of the Stables when in doubt, dear. He'll write dozens of letters—just you wait and see! I'm certain they'll start arriving to-morrow."

The Oracle of the Stables, like Homer, could sometimes nod. I had no letter from Joe next day. I was a little upset about this, so well had Mary succeeded in convincing me. However, I had no time to brood on my lack of mail, as I had all my belongings to transport on my bicycle handle-bars to the night V.A.D.'s home, a house that stood two miles from our day Mess. Kirsty was off from two until five that afternoon. She offered to help

115

me with my moving. "I thought we were supposed to be Mobile," she said, as she helped me strap one large suitcase on my handle-bars, and then held the bicycle steady as I got on. "How much more have you got?"

"Two more cases as big as this one, a holdall, a rug, a great-coat, a tennis-racket"—I rode round in circles to keep my balance—"and my wireless. I'll take that last, as I don't want to jolt it."

She said perhaps the Mobile part applied only to our persons. "How else can they expect us to carry a full indoor and outdoor uniform? Better not let Madam see what you have, though. She raised Cain when I arrived with my trunk. But how otherwise could I have brought my clothes down from Scotland?"

I said, much as I liked her company, I could never understand why they had sent her so far south. "There must be other military hospitals in the north. Look, I can't keep this up, Kirsty, I'm going to fall off. I don't mind falling, but my case may split, and then I'll have to pack all over again. That I could not take. I'll go ahead, and you catch me up."

She joined me with my holdall and rug on her handle-bars, and we cycled half the way together. We had to walk the other half, as it was uphill. The night house stood alone on top of the hill, a little back from the road. We propped our cycles against the wall and walked in at the open front door.

A large, slatternly woman, who wore heavy pearl earrings, a soiled cotton dress, and dirty pink mules, came out of one of the downstairs rooms. She had a cigarette in her mouth. She shifted it to one corner as she greeted us. "Which of you is the new girl, ducks?"

I said I was. "I've got some more luggage to fetch. We've brought the first batch. Shall we leave it in the hall or take it up somewhere?"

"Might as well take it up to your room, ducks. I'll show you the way. We'll have to go quiet, as the other girl is sleeping."

She led us to the top of the house. "You're in one of the attics, ducks," she whispered, loudly opening the door; "not much class about it, but it's your own."

The tiny room had a sloping roof and a dormer window. It was furnished with one iron bedstead and three Army biscuits. Kirsty put down my holdall and looked about distastefully. "What do you sit on?"

"The bed, I imagine." I walked to the window. "At least the view's good."

The caretaker said it didn't do to be fussy, and she could see I was one of those who was going to make the best of things. "I'll fetch up your sheets and blankets now, ducks, and give you a hand with the bed." She padded off in her flapping mules, and we waited until her footsteps died away before venturing to talk.

Kirsty groaned, "Clare, she's a chip off the old block. She's going to be as bad as Madam."

I sniffed. "Worse. Madam is clean. Oh, well. Let's get on with our removals, Kirsty. I'm supposed to get some sleep to-day."

When we had eventually brought all my luggage the caretaker, who said her name was Agnes, invited us both to a cup of tea. "Drop in whenever you want a cup, ducks. I always keep the pot brewing. Your girl friend, too." She leered at Kirsty. "I bet you girls have a good time up in the hospital with all those men, eh? Nothing to stop you! Wish I was a bit younger. Always fancied doing a bit of nursing, I did. Just my luck to be too old for this war. You young girls have all the fun—that's what I say!"

The Military Families Hospital was a small, square, three-storey building standing about fifty yards from the main hospital. It was staffed at night by two Sisters and a V.A.D. Sister Mackenzie, the Senior Sister, was a qualified midwife as well as being an S.R.N.; her colleague, Sister Best, was an S.R.N. only. Miss Mackenzie presided principally over the maternity floor, which occupied the top storey; Miss Best was in charge of the children's ward, which with the duty-room and rows of essential cupboards occupied the second floor, and the two women's wards on the ground floor. One of the women's wards was reserved for sick Sisters, V.A.D.'s, and any A.T.S. who were considered too ill for the wing at M.O.Q.

"We never have more than half a dozen A.T.S. or V.A.D.'s in," explained Miss Best when she showed me round her domain on my first night, "you girls are all too healthy. We haven't many sick women in either, now that they are shifting the families out of the camp. In fact, if it were not for the mums and babes above Sister Mackenzie and I would spend the night twiddling our thumbs. We still get a lot of mums in, as they can't be shifted until they've had their babies. I reckon we'll be open for about another three months to deal with all the bookings, and then turn into an extension for the men. This camp may soon be too hot a spot for people to raise families."

"Are you a midwife, too, Sister?" I asked, not then being aware of her qualifications.

She grimaced. "I am not. And never will be if I can help it. Now you had better go upstairs and introduce yourself to Sister Mackenzie before you do the black-out. Sister will give you your instructions for the night. She's in charge, not I."

I thanked her, and went up the three flights of stairs feeling rather cheerful. Miss Best seemed a pleasant person; she was young, plump, and entirely lacking in the forbidding air which some Army Sisters appear to assume as part of their uniform. Miss Mackenzie at first sight was very different from Miss Best.

She was English, despite her name; she was very tall and very fair, and her hair was pulled tightly back in a neat bun that was hidden beneath her cap, her eyes were large, blue, and cool in expression. She was young, possibly as young as Miss Best, but she was infinitely more dignified. Her manner reminded me a little of Miss Thanet in the Ob. Block. She considered me gravely. "Have you done any night duty previously, Miss Dillon?"

"I did a month in the Acute Medical Block, Sister."

"Good. But you have never worked in Families?"

"No, Sister." I noticed the badge of her training school that she wore pinned to her breast, and recognized it as the same as the badge worn by Miss Thanet. She saw my glance. "Do you know my hospital?"

"Matthew and Mark's? I don't know it, Sister, but my father qualified there. And Miss Thanet, too."

"You knew Miss Thanet?" She unbent slightly. "She was in my year. Where did you work with her? Ob. Block?"

"Yes, Sister."

She smiled. "You are that Dillon? Yes, I remember Miss Thanet mentioning you." She did not say what Miss Thanet had mentioned. "Now, we must go round the midwifery department, and I will show you what I shall want you to do for my mothers." She showed me in detail, explaining everything as she went. Then she took me into the nursery, in which the new-born babies lay asleep in cots that were fixed waist-high to the walls, and looked very like sloping pigeon-holes. "Put on a mask." She handed me one from the glass jar by the door, and tied one on herself. "Keep a mask round your neck all night. It saves so much time. You will work in here a good deal helping me with changing, feeding, bathing. Ever bathed a tiny baby?"

"No, Sister."

She looked at me calmly. "Ever held a tiny baby?"

"No, Sister."

She was unmoved. "I'll have to show you. Both are quite simple. How old are you?"

"Twenty, Sister."

"I see." She walked across the nursery and opened a door on the far side. "This is the Labour Ward." She did not go in, but stood in the open doorway. "Now, Miss Dillon, there is something I have to tell you at once. There is an official regulation applying to young V.A.D.'s working in Families. As you are unskilled, unmarried, and under age, you must not under any circumstances enter the Labour Ward when I am delivering a mother. That is official. Do you understand me?"

I felt very grateful to the unknown official who had laid down that order. "Yes, Sister."

Her large, serious blue eyes did not waver as she went on. "There is also something else I must tell you at once. There is only one bell in Families that is ever rung three times; three short rings. That is the Labour Ward bell, and that ring is the Labour Ward SOS. If you ever hear me ring like that drop whatever you are doing and run as fast as you can to me. SOS's have to be answered whatever the regulations may say. A mother's or a baby's life may depend upon it. Do you understand that too?"

I swallowed. "Yes, Sister."

"Good. Now go and do all the black-outs—excluding the Labour Ward, which I will do—then heat the milk for the night drinks. Sister Best will see to her own wards; you must see to my mothers, who will need their milk before they feed their babies." She glanced at the window. "It looks as if it's going to be a clear night, so I don't think we need bother about the P.A.D. routine yet. We'll go into that later to-night. Oh, by the way—just one more word of warning . . ."

"Yes, Sister?" I waited, wondering if she was going to warn me about what not to do when assisting at the birth of a baby.

"Have you any serious views on cockroaches?"

"Cockroaches, Sister?"

"Yes." She removed her cape and rolled up her sleeves. "Because if you have you had better get rid of them. You'll simply have to learn to love the wretched insects here. There's no alternative if you wish to retain your sanity. They come out in all the ground-floor passages at night, and particularly do they love the kitchen. We've used every insect powder that's been invented; the office have sent over squads of men to deal with them; nothing so far has been successful. Our Families cockroaches," she said evenly, "are extremely tough. The technique in the kitchen is to switch on the light before you go in at night, wait a few seconds, and then some of them do scatter. If they really bother you, providing the black-out's intact, you may leave the kitchen light burning all night. That does discourage them a little."

I went downstairs feeling far more worried about the cockroaches than a summons to the Labour Ward. It took me some time to do all the black-outs as I was new to the building, and when I reached the kitchen it was growing dark. I did not dare switch on the light before blacking out, so I stepped rather gingerly into the room. The floor under my feet crackled as if I were walking on gravel. I reached for the light-switch in sheer panic, forgetting the black-out, and when the light was on, for the first and only time in my life I wanted to scream in horror. The floor was black with the creatures, and the black carpet swayed towards me as if to attack me for the havoc I had caused

119

—there were some dozen black corpses under my feet. I leapt out of the kitchen and stood in the corridor outside, drying my damp palms on my apron skirt. I was sweating with fear; I did not think I should ever be able to go back into that kitchen and do the black-out, or put on the milk. Eventually I went back, not because I had conquered my fear, but because I had to. Once back I discovered that Mackenzie was right; the light did disturb them, and after a while the majority scuttled away into their holes. It took me several nights to get over that initial horror, and eventually, although I never learnt to love them, I grew to accept them, and even respect them. As Mackenzie said, they were so tough, and they seemed to thrive on the more deadly types of insect powder. I used pounds and pounds of powder, and the cockroaches grew fatter and more numerous, if possible.

On that first night Miss Best came in as I was filling the water urn. "Have you made tea, Dillon?"

"Not yet, Sister. That small kettle's boiling, if you'd like me to make some now?"

"Would you? Thanks." She set a tray for her patients. "Three of my women are pining for a cup."

"Doesn't it keep them awake?"

"They've enough on their minds to do that already, poor dears. They're all soldiers' wives, some of their husbands are still missing, they've got children parked with neighbours to fret over, and on top of that the worry of having to move house as the Army wants their quarters. The tea'll only soothe them." She poured boiling milk into some of her cups. "They're a good lot and don't grumble, but the War's miserable for them."

"Are your women always good patients, Sister?"

She held the milk saucepan poised and smiled at me through the steam. "Have you nursed women, Dillon?"

"No, Sister. Even when I did my fifty hours I was in a men's ward."

She said, "Then you've got a surprise coming to you. I expect you think men make the best patients?"

"Well—they are awfully good, Sister."

"I know. And that's what we all thought—until we nursed women. Men can be very good; women can be even better than that. The person who started the talk about women being the weaker sex had never set foot in a hospital ward. You'll find out for yourself. You don't have to take my word for it."

My first couple of weeks in Families were free of raids. I was glad about that, as it gave me a chance to learn what I had to do. The work was so very different from any I had done previously, chiefly because it was all nursing. No cleaning was done by the night V.A.D., much to my joy. I liked working with Miss Best—she was gay, good-natured, and she treated me as a

120

companion and not a subordinate. Miss Mackenzie, on the contrary, was aloof and very reserved, but I preferred working with her, as she was an inspired teacher. She taught me more general nursing in my first week than I had learnt in all my previous months in the main hospital. She never gave an order without explaining exactly how she wanted that order to be carried out; she showed me how to change, bath, and feed her babies; she showed me the quickest and easiest way to remove bloodstains from sheets; how to deal with soiled infant napkins; how to think ahead and save my feet; "never go anywhere empty-handed, Dillon," was one of her maxims; another was that new-born babies require cuddling on occasions. "Give him a little love, Dillon, then he'll settle down. The poor sweetie wants his mum, that's all."

I found myself respecting Mackenzie more than any woman with whom I had yet worked. I told Mary about her on the telephone. "She's quite something, Mary. She never lets her hair down, or drops her standards one inch. She even puts on her cuffs to eat our midnight snack of scrambled eggs. We eat them every night, cooking them over the duty-room fire as we used to cook in the Ob. Block. And she's only twenty-six! I can't get over it."

Mary said, "I've always heard that Matthew and Mark's produced the best results. They're terribly fussy there, but it must pay off. Incidentally, Agatha's been accepted. She's leaving at the end of the month and starting there in the September set."

"September? That's ages to go. Why is she having such a long leave?"

"It's August already, dear. Or have you forgotten?"

"Is it really?" I was astonished. "I've lost all account of time. I thought we were still in early July."

"Time always stands still on nights. How's Joe?"

"Well may you ask! I don't know. He hasn't written. So much for Joe's promises."

"He hasn't written?" She sounded aghast. "I don't believe it."

"It's true. Not one word have I had. I'm feeling good and narked."

"Are you now? That's interesting."

"Why?" I demanded, more sharply than I could have wished. I was very hurt that Joe had not written, but I did not want to admit that.

"The effect of absence is always interesting."

"Are you going to tell me it makes the heart grow fonder? Spare me that, Mary, please. Leave it to Madam."

"I wasn't going to say that. I was going to say something else. Speak French?"

121

"You know I can only discuss the aeroplane of my uncle the dive-bomber."

"Sorry. I forgot. They've got a saying——"

"They always have!" I interrupted rudely.

She told me to pipe down, please. "This one's quite good. Roughly, they say absence affects love, like a wind affects a flame. It blows out the little ones and blows up the big ones. What do you think of that?"

"My mother doesn't let me use the word."

She laughed. "You are cross, Clare. I've never known you cross before. You must be in love."

"You've got love on the brain. I'm just on nights. That makes me unfit for human companionship in the daytime. I must rush now, Mary, as supper's ready and Madam'll flap if I'm late. I'll ring you some other time."

"Do that. And don't be too cross with Joe. There is a war on, remember?"

"I'll remember," I said wearily. I did not want to talk any more about Joe. I felt thoroughly bad-tempered, and I stormed into the dining-room wishing that I had held to my original opinion of him. First thoughts, I decided, helping myself to tea, were always right. In future I would pay attention to them.

I was fuming over my third cup of tea when Madam came into the dining-room. "Dillon here? Dillon, m'dear, telephone. Bustle along, it's a trunk call."

I raced back to the telephone room, and felt a cold hand clutch at my stomach. I was sure it was my mother with news about Luke or Charles. I had been too annoyed with Joe lately to remember to worry about the boys. I should have remembered I had real worries from which habit had only removed the edge, and not wasted so much time looking for letters that had never come. I picked up the receiver, quite convinced of my caller's identity: "Hallo, Mother darling. Clare here."

"Clare?" It was Joe's voice. "I'm sorry I'm not your mother. How are you?"

"Joe!" I leant against the wall. "You gave me such a shock. What are you doing?"

"Ringing you up."

"I know that! Why? To say good-bye for ever again?"

There was a faint silence. Then, "Yes—and—no. I've got news for you. It seems the War can get on without me. I've worked my ticket. Just thought I'd let you know why I won't be writing from foreign parts."

"You've done—WHAT?"

"Dr Slaney," he answered calmly, "as from this afternoon."

"Joe. Stop fooling. What is all this?"

"Not fooling at all. It's quite true. I'm out. Bowler hat and all."

122

"But, Joe—why? You can't leave the Army. No one can. We're in it for the duration."

"Not Slaney. I've been sacked. Maybe it's because I lack moral fibre! You'd agree to that, surely?"

I frowned at the wall. "I'd agree to shaking you if you were within reach. Will you just be sensible for one minute and explain why you're out of hospital?"

"I didn't say I was out of hospital. On the contrary. I just said"—his voice sounded queer—"I was out of a job."

"But you have to be having a baby or have something like T.B. to get chucked out?"

He laughed. "Bright girl. You're catching on at last. For the record—I am not having a baby."

Slowly I understood. "That cough of yours—and your always looking so tired—is that why?"

"That's why. Some chap decided he didn't like the look of my unfortunate self, and insisted I had another medical. After that they handed me my ticket. Too easy."

"Joe, I really am sorry. Very sorry. How are you? Where are you? What are you going to do?"

"I'm at the end of a telephone. In a hospital. Somewhere. It seems as I've to stay in this hospital for the odd year or so. The chaps have been very decent. They aren't pitching me clean out into the cold, cold world, but into a nice clean sanatorium. I got down here this afternoon after my final Board. Even had an ambulance to myself. There's luxury for you."

I said, "I'm glad they've been nice, and I'm glad you're being looked after—but where are you?"

"I'm around. I only rang you to tell you the score, because I didn't want you thinking I was just shooting off my big mouth about loving you and then standing you up. I meant what I said, Clare, but I'd be obliged if you'd forget it. The incident is open and closed. I couldn't have been more accurate when I said I was speaking out of turn. I certainly was. Trust Slaney to jump the gun."

"What do you mean? You must tell me where you are. I'll come and see you—or something. I'd love to write. You can't just vanish."

"Can't I?" he replied soberly. "I think I can. You're a nice girl, Clare; I'm not going to have you being nice to me. I'm fussy about my fine bugs; I'm going to keep them to myself. I'll see you around sometime, when I'm on my two feet."

"Joe—do stop being heroic! I've no patience with heroes! I never heard such nonsense in all my life! You can't just ring me up and tell me news like this and then disappear into thin air! How about your family? Are you going to be near them? Can't they fix that for you?"

"Sure, sure. They'll just order a special hospital ship to take yours truly across the Irish Sea. Don't be a moron, girl! Why the devil would I want to go back to Belfast on a stretcher? I'm not going to have my mother or anyone else spending all her spare time visiting my sick-bed. I've seen enough of relatives hanging round sick-beds. It's hell for the poor bastards. I'm not having any of that, believe you me. And don't tell me you're not one of my relatives—I know that. And I know what I'm doing. Damn you, Clare!" He was now as worked-up as I was. "I only rang you to explain why I wouldn't be writing! I don't want you weeping and wailing over me!"

"I've no intention of weeping and wailing over you! I'm just being civilized. If Mary, or Agatha, or any friend of mine got tubercle I'd do the same. I'd want to go and visit them if I could —bring 'em fruit and flowers and have a gossip."

He said he loathed fruit and abhorred flowers. "The gossip can keep. It can go into cold storage with a lot of other things?"

"Until—when?"

"And how would I know? Whoever heard of anyone telling a patient anything? This year, next year, some time, never. It'll be in the book."

"Which book?" I asked idiotically, my mind now being occupied with the full realization of what he was saying. He did not answer me immediately; he seemed to be having a conversation with someone his end. I heard him say, "I'll do that, Sister. Thanks for lending me your office." Then his voice was more clear. "What's that you said, Clare?"

"I said—which book?"

"Oh, hell, darling! The book-from-which-there-is-no-rubbing-out. What other book would I mean? I have to stop now, they want the 'phone. Cheers, girl. I'm glad we met. Take care of yourself on that bike of yours. The rate you go one day you'll bump yourself off for sure. And that's all I have to say." There was a faint click as he rang off.

I jiggled the telephone furiously. "Exchange? Can you tell me where that call came from, please?"

"Sorry, miss. We don't keep a check on incoming calls. I can only tell you it was a trunk. That any help?"

"Not much. Thanks all the same." I replaced the instrument thoughtfully. I wondered how much Joe had left unsaid, not about myself, but about his illness. How badly had he got it? I remembered the men in the Acute Medical Block. Three-quarters of those men had been tubercle patients when I worked there. Joe had sounded quite normal; they often sounded perfectly normal, even when they were moribund.

The ill-temper and depression from which I had suffered all evening vanished. I was suddenly wildly angry. I cursed aloud the silent telephone, the exchange, Joe, the War, and all men for being so downright childish. I used all the foul language I learnt, not from the troops, but from the M.O.'s and my fellow-V.A.D.'s. I discovered cursing did not relieve my feelings at all.

When I went on duty that night my anger remained white-hot. I was desperately sorry for Joe despite that anger, but his ostrich policy inflamed me more with each passing minute. What good did he think he was doing himself? He knew, far better than I, how important a boosted morale is to all patients, particularly to anyone suffering from a long, lingering illness like his. He was going to need every available ally; and he thought he could fight alone. Dimly I could grasp why he was acting in this way; I understood because of my brothers. I knew that in most young men there was a hidden Galahad who could on occasions come to the surface and make a man behave in a highly chivalrous and utterly impractical manner. Joe planned to fade gracefully from my life since he was now technically a burden, without stopping to ask whether I wanted any part of that burden. In fairness I had reluctantly to admit that he could have no notion that I did; but I refused to be placated. His cloak and dagger act was maddening, and going to be a waste of time, since I intended to pull every string and ask questions, if necessary of every M.O. and Q.A. in the hospital. Someone here was bound to have some friend on the staff of the hospital in which Joe had been boarded. Failing that, there was Mary, who had dozens of Army connexions; and if he was in a civilian hospital Uncle Michael might be able to help. My father had had ex-colleagues from Matthew and Mark's in practically every large hospital in the country. Someone would be able to track down exactly where Joe was for me, but it was going to take so much time, and time was something I had not got. The nights in Families were always busy, and in the day I was too sleepy to do more than climb the stairs to my attic and fall asleep. Agnes always had to shake me to life in the evening; if she did not do that I would simply sleep on.

I cursed round the kitchen, slamming on saucepans and kettles, ignoring the cockroaches unless they dared get under my feet. The unfortunate insects who proved daring were destroyed ruthlessly. For once the disgusting crackling sound left me unmoved. Miss Best came in for her tray. "You seem to be having a field day, Dillon. What's all the noise about? By the sound of it you're having a private air-raid in here."

"Sorry, Sister." I dumped the heavy urn on the gas, spilling some of the water on my apron. "Oh, blast! Sorry." I apologized again. "I'm in a flaming temper. I didn't realize I was making such a noise."

"What's wrong?" She set her tray. "Didn't you sleep to-day?"

"Like a top, thanks. No. It's something that's cropped up this evening"—and as I had to put my Fifth Column into action some time, I told her about Joe. "Have you ever heard anything so idiotic, Sister?"

"Illness often makes young men want to act like heroes at the outset. They don't appreciate the difficulties their heroics can make for themselves and other people. You get this sort of thing in the wards; a man swears blind he's not in pain—as if you can't recognize when anyone's in pain! But no. He'll grit his teeth and hang on, feeling very brave, and all that happens is that finally you have to give him twice as much dope to knock out the pain, it takes twice as long to have effect, and gives all concerned twice as much work. And this young man of yours is an M.O.? He would be. Doctors always make the most difficult patients."

"Yes. I've heard that." I let her qualification pass. People would be more disposed to help me if Joe was officially considered my young man.

"Was he ever stationed here? Do I know him?"

"I expect so, Sister. Joe Slaney."

"Joe Slaney's got tubercle! Dillon, I am sorry! But now I come to think it over—I'm not surprised. Poor man. No wonder he's been walking round looking like death these last few months. I wonder if he guessed he had it?"

"I don't know." I remembered that afternoon he had fainted, and how he had insisted that I ignore his faint afterwards; I remembered how exhausted he often looked, and his leisurely air that had once irritated me. A man saving his strength would move as Joe had moved. Above all, I remembered the way he never touched me; that last evening in his car he had sat as far away from me as he could, and when he had coughed he had leant out of the window. "I don't know. I think he may have had a hunch."

"I think you're right." She looked at me. "I'm remembering something Sister Theatre once said about Slaney's passion for wearing two masks in the theatre. I expect he wanted to be on the safe side—just in case. Of course, it's so easy to be wise now, but someone should have insisted on his chest being screened before. Only I suppose everyone's been too busy these last few months to bother to notice the M.O.'s. It's rotten luck for him. And so you're the girl he was keen on? We knew he was keen on someone, but not whom. How long has this been going on between you?"

"Not long. Sister, where do you think he had his Board? Millbank?"

"Possibly. Could be elsewhere. He didn't even tell you that?"

"No."

"But, of course, you want to know where he is to be able to visit him?"

"Yes."

"You're not frightened of picking up his bugs?"

"Not after working in the A.M. Block."

"Fair enough." She lifted her tray-load of cups. "I've got a friend at Millbank. A girl I trained with. Like me to ask her if she knows anything about Slaney?"

"Would you, Sister? Thanks."

"I will. We'll ask Sister Mackenzie, too. Perhaps she can get something out of Major Scott when he does his night rounds. But there's just one point." She stopped in the doorway and turned to look at me. "Forgive my asking this, Dillon, but are you certain you want to find where he is, and visit him? If you do manage that you're going to give him ideas. A man in a hospital bed has plenty of time for thinking and hoping; he's also the easiest person in the world to lead up the garden path. I have no brief for young women who do that kind of thing; it's not fair to raise a man's hopes just because you feel sorry for him and fancy yourself as a visitor of the sick. Pity is not enough to offer a man who's fond of you; it can only hurt instead of help. Are you quite certain this desire to find him is not something that's been born out of the heat of the moment?"

I thought this over. "It has come to me in the heat of the moment, Sister," I said at last, "but I am quite sure that it's what I want to do."

Her smile was extraordinarily kind. "Then we'd best find Slaney for you. I think your news will do his chest a power of good. We'll talk to Sister Mackenzie about it at supper."

8

BABIES, BOMBS, AND
COCKROACHES

MISS MACKENZIE knelt on the hearth as she toasted the bread of our scrambled eggs. "The man who really could give us the answer is Tommy Lomax." She removed a piece of toast from the end of the long fork and substituted for it a piece of bread. "You know whom I mean, Best? 'Lungs' Lomax; the great Sir Thomas. He's a nice man for all that, and we think he knows more about chests than anyone in the country. I'm almost certain he's at Millbank; I know he was there. He's been in the Army since February. He may even have seen Joe Slaney yesterday."

Miss Best asked the question I did not like to ask. "That's all very fine, Mac, but how does Dillon contact your Sir Thomas? She can hardly write to him out of the blue. Surely there's someone lower down the scale whom we can tackle?"

Miss Mackenzie said she had not expected me to write to Sir Thomas Lomax. "I was thinking of that friend of yours, Best. She's on the spot. She could ask someone to ask old Tommy, or ask him herself. He's a very approachable man, and not at all like a pundit." She wrinkled her smooth forehead. "I don't believe I know one woman up there now. Everyone I know has gone overseas. But perhaps we won't have to go to such lengths; Major Scott may know all about it. He's very late for his round, but I'll try and ask him when he comes. If he hasn't heard tonight he may hear in a day or two. These things always get round the inter-hospital grape-vine." She handed another piece of toast to Miss Best, who was now presiding over the butter. "Are the eggs coming along, Dillon? Toast's finished."

"Be ready in a few seconds, Sister." I removed the saucepan from the fire and beat the eggs furiously. "They're setting now."

Miss Mackenzie pushed three chairs round the fire as I dished up the eggs. We always ate our midnight meal in the small office on the second floor, since we were unanimous in our dislike of sharing a meal with the cockroaches.

"I do enjoy this eating in peace," said Best, settling down with a tray on her lap. "You've brought us quiet nights, Dillon. We've not had one baby, or one bomb, to disturb our supper since you came on nights."

Miss Mackenzie rolled her eyes. "My dear Best—what a thing to say! I'll probably have twins at least before I've finished half my eggs."

"Are you expecting any babies to-night, Sister?" I asked. "Could I have the salt, please?"

"I've got two who might come off, but I don't really expect they will until morning, so long as we don't have a raid. Nothing like a raid for bringing on a baby. Is there any pepper?"

"I'm afraid not, Sister. The pepper tin was empty. I couldn't find any in the cupboard, but if you like I'll go down and have another look."

"I can do without it, thanks. It isn't fair to disturb the cockroaches in the middle of their meal. They're probably keeping their fingers crossed like we are, that no large feet will come and trample in their midst. Not that you've got large feet, Dillon," she added politely, "but only because any foot that can squash the life out of a dozen of its fellows must strike a cockroach as large."

Miss Best laughed. "Mac, I do believe you like those monsters!"

"Like them, nothing! I just have a fellow-feeling with them. We're all in the same boat—three million cockroaches and us three. Can we have a meal in peace? Can we get through our night undisturbed? Will some tiresome giant come and knock our heads in? Our problems are identical." She glanced at me. She was being much more approachable to-night, and I guessed I had Joe to thank for it. My relationship with Joe had admitted me to the closed circle of Sisters, M.O.'s, and M.O.'s wives and young women. "With the addition of your unusual problem, Dillon, I really am very sorry to hear about Joe Slaney. I'm not an old pal of his or anything, but I was in the Theatre Block when he was there. Immediately before I came on nights here. I didn't see much of him, but he seemed a pleasant type, and I liked the way he took his work seriously. He really cared about the men. I like doctors who care about their patients." She put her tray on the floor beside her and stretched her arms. "Oh, I am so tired! Roll on my nights off. I'm going to sleep and sleep." She swept her great cape over the back of her chair and relaxed comfortably. "This is sheer bliss. You make good coffee, Dillon." She smiled at me as she spoke. "What's the matter? What are you listening to? One of my babes crying?"

"No, Sister. Listen"—I held up a hand—"can you hear what I hear?"

We could all hear the same sound now. Miss Mackenzie stood up. "I thought it was too good to last! The spell is broken. Here we go, girls—and there goes the sleep of my poor mums. Thank the Lord, the babes will sleep through anything.

Miss Best pulled off her cap and took her tin hat from its peg on the office wall. "Would this be an exercise or——" Her question was lost in the sudden bark of gunfire. The noise of that first gun was immediately followed by the rising chorus of the camp air-raid sirens. "It would be." Miss Best answered herself. "And my tired ladies downstairs only got to sleep just before I came up." She slapped her hat on her head. "See you in the shelter, Dillon. Enjoy yourself, Mac. What do you bet you have both babies?"

"I never bet on a certainty," replied Mackenzie with dignity. She had removed her own cap, but held her tin hat in her hand. The light shone on her neat hair and made it shine like spun glass. "Get your helmet on, Dillon, then cope with the babes. Have you got your routine taped? Good girl. Get on with it. This may only be a false alarm, but it doesn't sound like it."

I put on my hat as instructed, slung my respirator case over my back like a school satchel, and went swiftly to the nursery.

The feeding-bottles filled with glucose-water that I prepared each night for just such an emergency as this were waiting on a white enamel tray by the babies' sterilizer. The whole tray was covered by a clean white towel, over which was laid a soft white blanket to keep in the heat. In the centre of the nursery each night I stood one of the large stretcher trolleys. Beneath the trolley was an unlit hurricane lamp; on the trolley was a box of matches. Every night at ten Miss Mackenzie checked the nursery to see that all the P.A.D. preparations for the new-born babies were complete.

The sirens were still screaming as I pocketed the matches and fixed the hurricane lamp on to one of the end-poles of the trolley; gunfire was now almost continuous, and behind the guns I could hear the noise of aeroplane engines. The babies all slept soundly. They did not wake at the noise, or when I lifted each in turn from a cot, rolled him or her in many shawls, and tucked them down, side by side and end to end on the trolley. Mackenzie had shown me how to load fourteen babies at a time on that trolley; the nursery held twenty-four cots; twenty of them were occupied that night. Mackenzie had told me always to take the maximum number. "You can't be certain of getting back for the rest, Dillon. Take out as many as you can at once."

I stopped momentarily to look back at the six babies I had to leave behind. "I'll come back just as soon as I can, sweeties," I said apologetically. The small, trusting little creatures slept on peacefully, the only people in the camp, perhaps, who were undisturbed by the hideous noise that was shattering the calm summer night.

The babies had priority in the lift; all the women who could be moved to the basement shelter used the stairs until all the babies were safely below ground. The shelter was well constructed, and as safe as any place could be from anything but a direct hit. The floor was lined with mattresses; piles of pillows, blankets, and magazines stood in heaps on the floor. There were no windows, but long ventilating shafts had been cut in the inside walls, and there were two doors. When I reached the shelter with my first trolley-load Best was there attending to her patients; wrapping shawls round their shoulders, blankets over their knees, and propping pillows behind their backs as they leant against the walls. Once she had moved all the patients that could be moved she returned to her wards to stay with those women who could not be moved. For convenience's sake—and for company—all these women were always warded in beds on the first ground-floor ward. Mackenzie never left the top floor at all. "You are O.C. shelter, Dillon," she had said, when she taught me the precautionary routine, "and that's not a hard job. The women are good and sensible; we've never had anyone lose her head yet. They sit and knit and swop ghastly stories about their innards and their husbands and make a positive mothers' meeting of it."

The raid did not last long that night. We could hear the aeroplanes, and the camp guns firing, but we never heard a bomb that sounded close. An hour later all the babies, still sleeping, were back in their cots; the women were drinking hot drinks in their beds; and I was causing havoc among the cockroaches in the kitchen, as I brewed more tea, cocoa, and reheated our supper coffee.

For several nights those minor raids continued, and we became thoroughly annoyed with the Germans. "It's not that I've anything against Jerry," explained Best, "but my poor women are getting exhausted. How can they get well? They never get a proper night's sleep!"

Mackenzie yawned. "What's the moon doing?"

"On the wane, Sister."

"Oh, no! That does it! When the moon goes in the 'planes come out. Haven't you noticed? Major Scott was saying that only last night—and that reminds me, Dillon—I've asked him twice about Joe Slaney and he hasn't heard a thing. In fact, I gave him the news. He's promised to keep an ear to the ground and let me know if he hears anything."

I thanked her, a little wearily. I was feeling very tired myself that night. I had stopped sleeping like the dead in the daytime; I now slept very badly indeed, and the agony of trying to sleep in the day was near to the agony of trying to keep awake at night. I never dared sit down on my own for one moment during the night; if I did my head instantly began to drop as the demanding waves of sleep enveloped me, and the effort of forcing myself to rise above those waves and stay awake was growing beyond my power. So I stayed on my feet.

Mackenzie, who looked as tired as I felt, noticed what I was holding. "What do you think you are doing carrying a cup and saucer without a tray, Dillon? Go and get a tray at once! Never let me see you carrying anything like that again. I will not have it!"

I went back to the kitchen for the tray, feeling very peeved with life and more than a little sorry for myself. What did a tray matter? Oddly enough, I discovered the answer in a few minutes. The young woman to whom I took the now reheated cup of milk was a newly delivered mother. She snuggled against her pillows contentedly. "Sister said as she'd ask you to fetch me a drop of milk, Nurse. It does look nice on that pretty little tray! Like as I was having my baby in a posh nursing-home. You nurses are so good to us—the trouble you take! It makes ever such a difference, dear."

After which I felt hideously ashamed, and vowed inwardly that I would never move without a tray, and if possible a lace doily, for the rest of the War.

Next morning I rang Mary to ask if her Army strings had been any good.

"I've got my father-in-law working on it, dear. He may be able to come up with something."

After ringing her I wrote to Uncle Michael. I was not hopeful now; lack of sleep was making me very depressed; but I was happier writing letters than trying to sleep through the heat of the day when the sun on the roof directly above my room turned the attic into an oven. That night the moon had gone, and, as Mackenzie had forecast, the bombers came out. At eleven the sirens began; the raid was mercifully short, and the women and babies were back in bed before midnight. They had not been in their beds one hour before the alert sounded again.

I groaned aloud to the baby I was feeding. "You've had your chips, love. Back to the basement." I put down his bottle, and he roared in protest. "It's no good, son." I held him against my shoulder, and patted his back to comfort him. "Dinner's adjourned." With the baby boy still in my arms, I pulled off my cap, slapped on my tin hat, which I had left on the napkin cupboard, removed my respirator from the nursery door-handle, and slung it over my shoulder. "You and I have got to make tracks, son, so just you stay on that trolley like a good boy, while I collect your little pals."

The baby disapproved of this interruption loudly, and I did not blame him at all. I only longed to be able to open my mouth and bellow as he was bellowing. He did not stop shouting until I began wheeling the loaded trolley to the lift, then he gave a contented little murmur as if to say he approved of nocturnal pram rides.

Best's women were already busy knitting when we reached the

shelter. "What a life, eh, Nurse? Still, I'll get the heel of me sock turned if nothing else!"

When I went up for the second lot of babies Best stopped the lift at the first floor. "Keep an extra eye on my women for me, will you, Dillon? I won't be able to go down to them at all. That first raid nearly gave my poor Mrs Sinclair another coronary. She's quite blue, and I've fixed up the oxygen for her. I daren't leave her for more than a few seconds. Are my women all right? I had to bundle them down on their own, and they swore they could cope, but I hated doing it."

"They've settled themselves, Sister. I thought you must have seem to them. They're all knitting."

"Thank God for whoever invented knitting-needles! I'll be with Mrs Sinclair and the others. Remember," she added calmly, "if anyone wants to know, there are seven of us in that first ward."

"Right, Sister. I'll tell them." I closed the lift doors and went upward to the top floor. When I arrived at the midder floor one of the mothers walked unsteadily out of the ward. "The Sister told us to come out to you, Nurse. She said to tell you she can't leave Mrs Ellis, and you'll tell us where to go. Do we go down in the lift?"

I hesitated. She did not look strong enough to use the stairs. A bomb shook the building as I looked at her. "That's right, dear," I said, as the noise of the crash subsided. "Are there any more of you to come?"

"Five more, Nurse." Her voice shook slightly, as the building had done. "Here they come."

None of them looked fit to face the stairs. I took the law into my own hands, helped them into the lift, closed the gates, and pushed the button, having asked them to be sure to close the lift gates when they reached the basement. "Wait for me down there," I called, as the lift disappeared, then pushed my trolley at the double along to the nursery to collect the rest of the babies.

When we were all in the shelter the women discussed the raid. They were convinced there would be another to-night. "Bound to go in threes, it is! Listen to that!" The noise was muffled by the building over our heads and the thick walls around us, but it could not be hidden. It was the noisiest raid I had ever heard. The women agreed with me. "Someone's catching it to-night, Nurse. Did you hear that? That was a near one!"

I looked at their faces; they were all sick women; they would not have been in hospital when beds were so precious had they not been ill; their faces were pale only with illness and fatigue. No one screamed; no one cried; no one looked scared. They were so busy knitting and exchanging recipes. "You want to beat the eggs first dear, then let them stand while you work the paste. But it's the beating that——" The speaker had to stop as another bomb crashed close at hand; she took a deep breath, and continued as soon as she could be heard. "As I was saying, dear, it's the beating that makes all the difference. That's my secret."

One of the babies began to cry. I picked her up and sat down on the mattress-covered floor to feed her. The woman next to me had not yet had her baby. She bent over the small girl in my arms. "Isn't that Mrs Brown's June? Lovely baby, isn't she, Nurse! Can I feed her for you?"

I saw the expression in her eyes. I handed her June Brown. "That is kind of you, Mrs Jay. Thank you."

Mrs Jay started something. In a few minutes my trolley was clear of babies; shortly after that, the babies lying side by side on their shared mattress were also moved. The babies snuggled down in the women's arms, as babies do snuggle when they feel they are being loved, and the women bent over them with the gentle expressions women reserve for new babies. I heard snatches of whispered conversations: "There, there, lovey—I'll hold you for your mum." "There's a fine little lad. Got a smile for Aunty, have you? I won't say it's the wind either!" "That's it, girlie, you have a nice little snooze. That's right. I'll rock you to sleep." And rock and croon they did, as if they were all in their own private nurseries, while all round us and above us all hell was let loose.

All hell and three bells ringing sharply. The shelter bell indicator jangled urgently, the red flap marking the Labour Ward swung violently.

The women asked, "Sister ringing for you, Nurse, dear?"

I jumped up unwillingly, not reluctant to answer that ring, but to leave them. "I'll have to go to Sister. Will you ladies mind? I'll be back as soon as I can. Will you just all stay in here whatever happens until one of the staff gets down to you? It's a very good shelter. You'll be all right—so long as you stay in here."

They said I was not to give them another thought. "We're all nice and comfortable, dear, and we'll look after your babies for you. You're not to worry about us—but we don't like to think of you and the poor Sisters upstairs."

"Bless you." I took the box of matches from my pocket and gave them to an A.T.S. sergeant who was one of Miss Best's patients. "These are for this." I moved the hurricane lamp by her. "If the lights go out can you light it, Sergeant?"

"I can. O.K." She had to move carefully, because she still had stitches in. "I'll keep an eye on things," she murmured more quietly. "Good luck, Nurse."

"You too." We smiled at each other. "Thanks."

I ran along the basement corridor and up the three flights of stairs as fast as I could. Mackenzie looked up as I pushed open the double doors of the Labour Ward.

"Take that wretched tin hat off, Dillon," she said quietly, "or you may drop it on Junior. The mask jar is by your right hand. Put on a clean mask, wash your hands, and come here." When I had obeyed her she said, "Put your hands on top of mine in the same position as mine are. I must be free to move. That's it."

As she slipped her hands from beneath mine a bomb whistled over the roof. Mackenzie glanced at me momentarily; she did not duck, she merely took a fresh grip on the baby's head. As she remained upright I did also, despite the fact that every instinct I possessed was demanding that I get under something quickly. The sound of the bomb exploding was a glorious relief to me, but the terrified young mother screamed with terror and began to twist her body on the flat bed.

Mackenzie muttered, "Blast the b——s!" Then called aloud, "Take it easy, my dear, you're doing very well! That's it—just a little longer—that's it, good girl—another pain coming—that's it—you're being so good—you won't have to stand much more—here we are——" Her voice rose, partly in triumph, and partly to be heard above the barrage of anti-aircraft fire. "It's a girl! A nice little girl!" She tied the cord twice and reached for her scissors. "A honey of a baby with black curly hair! Masses of hair, and all complete! Aren't you a clever young mum to have produced such a fine little daughter!"

The mother opened her eyes and her mouth. She was smiling, and she seemed to be talking, but we could not hear what she was saying, because a second near explosion, even louder than the first, was shaking the hospital and making the Labour Ward rattle as if it were a toy being rattled by an irate child. The bottles on the white china shelves that had survived until now jangled like bells, then crashed and spilt their contents on the floor. The light above the delivery bed swayed as if we were on a rolling ship at sea, and the light folding cradle that was standing open and waiting by the bed slipped a couple of feet on the polished floor.

Mackenzie hitched it forward with her foot. "Don't move your hands until I say so, Dillon," she said, and went on with what she was doing.

The girl on the bed was now oblivious to the raid. She smiled and smiled; her flushed face was illuminated with sheer radiance. "Did you say a girl, Sister?" she asked in the next lull. "Oh, Sister, I am glad. Her dad will be too. We wanted a girl. Thank you so much."

135

Mackenzie's blue eyes were anything but cold as she smiled back. "Always happy to oblige, Mrs Ellis. All part of the service." She held the naked little baby up in her arms. "Come along young woman. What have you got to say for yourself?"

The baby replied with a magnificent squawk that bore no resemblance to the faint wail I had been expecting as all that a new-born baby could produce. The squawk altered to an out-raged yell. Mackenzie rolled her in a towel and then a blanket, and laughed. "I don't blame you at all, ducks," she said, carrying the infant to the mother, "I'd yell blue murder if anyone hauled me into the world on a night like this. Now meet your brave mum. Here, my dear"—she tucked the baby into her mother's open arms—"meet your little daughter."

Mrs Ellis gave a soft gasp. "Oh, Sister——" She touched the baby's petal-soft face with one finger. "Oh, Sister—oh, Sister——" she repeated over and over again.

For a few seconds Mackenzie stood looking down at the mother and child; her gold head was still capless, her face was half covered by her mask, her eyes were serene. An air of con-tentment filled the Labour Ward, making me ignore, rather than forget, the raid that was still going on. I felt as if the noise was merely a too loud wireless that needed turning down; I did not think I was alone in that feeling. For those few seconds three women had forgotten the War as we shared the victory and wonder and happiness that can come with the birth of a healthy baby.

Mackenzie said, "I'll take that position from you, Dillon. Move your hands from under mine as I did. Then fix that black-out on the window behind you. I've just noticed it's come away again. There's a jinx on that window. It just refuses to stay black-outed. Use adhesive on it."

It took a whole roll of two-inch strapping to get that black-out screen in position again. "I think it'll stay now, Sister."

"Hope so." Mackenzie glanced over her shoulder as she stood at the sink examining the after-birth. "I've at least one more baby coming off to-night, and this raid looks as if it's going on until dawn. By the sound of it they're coming in close again. Is that the office 'phone I hear?"

"Shall I go and find out, Sister?"

"Yes, but don't loiter in the passage. Those windows outside have taken a shaking to-night. They may give."

I did not loiter in the passage; I ran along to the office. The telephone bell was ringing furiously. I raised the receiver and held it away from my ear until the ringing had stopped. "Families, night V.A.D. speaking."

"Nurse!" The voice the other end was as furious as the bell had sounded. "This is the Garrison P.A.D. officer. You are showing a light in a top-storey room on the west side. Will you please see to it, instantly."

I explained that the screen had become dislodged by the blast. "We have just mended it."

"About time too! It should have been seen to directly it fell down. Kindly ask Sister to be sure that no light is shown again."

Miss Mackenzie received this request with a curt nod. "Do you suppose the silly so-and-so thinks I have time in the middle of a delivery to start playing with black-out screens? All right, Dillon. Thanks. It's fixed now, so perhaps he'll relax. Now will you take this infant, wrap her in blankets as I showed you, put her in her cot by her mum, then mark two wristbands with her name, Rose Ellis, date, time of birth—that was 1.10 A.M.—and sew one on each wrist. When you've done that go back to the shelter."

"Do I take the baby with me, Sister?"

She looked across to Mrs Ellis, who was lying with her eyes closed, and shook her head. "For one thing—the corridor and lift are too draughty; for another—I never part them at this stage. Mrs Ellis will have to stay up; she can't go gallivanting in lifts after the amount she's lost; a little more and we'll have a P.P.H. on our hands. She must lie still, and her babe must stay where her mum can see her."

The women in the shelter were enchanted to hear Mrs Ellis had a daughter. "There, she did so want a girl! Is she to be called Rose, Nurse? Ever such a pretty name, it is! And how lucky she's been to have that Sister Mackenzie to deliver her. She wanted it to be Sister Mackenzie. She's a lovely Sister, that Sister; ever so clever, for all she's so young. And you never catch that Sister getting in a state. Always cool as a cucumber, that's Sister Mackenzie."

The alert lasted for an hour and a half longer. During that period the Labour Ward black-out fell down four times. I knew exactly when it fell down, even though I was in the basement, because the telephone in the basement corridor rang within a few seconds of the screen falling. "Garrison P.A.D. officer here! Will you please put that light out instantly as the screen is inefficient!" I went up to the Labour Ward after each message to hand it on to Mackenzie. With each message Mackenzie's actions continued calm, but her normally restrained language grew more purple. "Can I help it if the bloody Germans drop their bloody bombs all round this bloody camp, Dillon? Fix the b—— again! I must have a light. Both my women are coming off now. I'm just praying one will be five minutes ahead of the other; if not I'll have to ring for you again."

She rang her SOS fifteen minutes later. When I arrived panting in the Labour Ward she told me to wash quickly and put on

137

the rubber gloves she had laid out for me. "Then come here—get your fingers like mine—spread them, and get the head in the palm of your hand. That's it, now just let Junior do what he wants to, don't force anything, but hold the head steady." She stood up and smiled at the woman by whose bed we were bending. "That's it, my dear, Nurse knows just what to do—you're being very good—save your breath for the next pain—good girl——" She darted to the other bed, that was now only a yard away. Mrs Ellis and her baby had disappeared, I had no notion where. I concentrated on what Mackenzie had told me to do automatically; there was no question of my believing any of this, there was no time for belief, there was only time to act.

Mackenzie was talking to the other mother. "Now, dear—only one more pain, I think, and then——" She stopped, as the first bomb for several minutes dropped a fair distance off. The explosion helped both women, they gasped, relaxed, and their babies were born within a minute of each other and yelled their objections about life together.

Mackenzie moved like silent lightning between the beds. "Get the name tapes at once, Dillon, and tie them on. They're both boys. We won't worry about Christian names. Ginger here is Bevis; your chap is Taylor. Now, you're sure you've got that? Just see to their names, date, and time. That's right." She glanced up. "Congratulations, ladies. You've both got boys. Fine boys; all complete. Nice work, both of you." She rolled Master Bevis under her arm and gave him to his mother. "Here's a fine redhead for you, my dear. He's a splendid boy." Then she dealt with Master Taylor, whom I was holding. "Meet your son, Mrs Taylor. A tough if ever I saw one. Look at him doubling his fist already." She turned to me, and mopped her brow with the back of her forearm. "What time is it, Dillon?"

"Twenty to three, Sister."

"All-clear gone? The raid seems over."

I was surprised to discover the night had grown silent. I had not even been aware that the gunfire had stopped. "I'm not sure, Sister. I don't think I've heard it."

"I don't wonder." She tugged her mask down round her neck as if she needed air. She looked round the Labour Ward. "This place looks a shambles with all those smashed bottles."

"Shall I sweep them up, Sister?"

"No, they'll have to wait. I want you to do something else for me. I'll have to get Major Scott back. I'm not at all happy about Mrs Ellis." She looked very worried. "My bones tell me she's going to have that P.P.H. after all. Will you tell him that, and say I'd be grateful if he'd come, stat. For your information, stat means at once."

"Yes, Sister. Er—what's a P.P.H.?"

138

She smiled faintly. "Poor kid. I keep forgetting how green you are. A Post-partum Hæmorrhage, and a nasty thing. If he asks, she is grouped and we've got the blood. All right?"

The switchboard orderly was curt: "I can't get the Major, miss, not yet. He's operating. We're having a busy time, you know."

"Then get us the O.M.O., and quickly!" I snapped back. "And don't tell me there's a raid on. We know it. We also know that one of our mothers may be going to die. She's just had her first baby. How would you feel if she was your wife? If you can't get Major Scott get any M.O. over here quick as you can." I slammed down the receiver feeling better for my outburst. Oddly, until I lost my temper with that unfortunate orderly, I had no idea that I was feeling on edge at all.

The all-clear was sounding as I returned to the Labour Ward to tell Mackenzie of my telephone conversation. "Let's hope this means Major Scott can be over soon. The O.M.O.'s all right, but I'd rather have a specialist for a woman as ill as I'm afraid she may be going to be. Go and get your babes from the basement and help my mothers back to bed, and then perhaps we may be able to get some work done."

- The babies were all sleeping peacefully in the women's arms; they did not wake when they were transferred to the trolley and the mattress to await their turn on the trolley, so as the mothers looked exhausted I first helped them up in the lift, then went down for the trolley-load of babies. When they, still sleeping, were in their cots I returned for my final load. The basement lights went out while I was in the shelter. The A.T.S. sergeant had returned my matches to me, so I lit the hurricane lamp and hung it on the end of the trolley, stacked the babies, a bundle of spare shawls, and the tray of bottles on top, and pushed the trolley out of the shelter and along the now dark basement corridor. I felt suddenly dazed with fatigue; I could only think about Mrs Ellis, and whether Mackenzie was right, and she was going to bleed, and if she would bleed to death. She had looked so happy after her baby was born; it was such a nice baby, much nicer than the two red pug-faced little boys. My trolley hit something soft while I was remembering the ginger-headed baby I had helped into the world. I stopped still, momentarily too tired to be interested in what I had hit, since the trolley and the babies were intact. In the yellow light from the hurricane lamp I saw feet on the floor ahead. Feet in Army boots. The owners of the feet were silent, and they remained silent as I counted them. Ten feet, five pairs, five men. My brain worked very slowly. I lifted the lamp from the trolley to look at the men's faces. I discovered I recognized only two of them. One was Steve Heller, one of the M.O.'s; the other the R.S.M.,

Mr Smith. Beside Mr Smith stood a man with a belligerent expression and a major's crown on the shoulders of his battle-dress tunic.

The R.S.M. cleared his throat. "Morning, Miss Dillon. Garrison P.A.D. officer here. The Major's come to complain about the light that's been showing here to-night."

The garrison air defence officer was the next person to clear his throat. "It's been most disgraceful——" he began importantly. He could not go on. A voice from the head of the stair-well interrupted him. The voice belonged to Mackenzie.

"Dillon, what do you think you are doing, loitering down there with those babes? Do you want to give them pneumonia?"

The men's heads jerked upward as if they were puppets and Mackenzie had pulled their five strings. The light on the top floor had not gone out, and we could see the outline of her fair, still capless, head clearly.

I said, "The Garrison P.A.D. officer is down here, Sister. He has come to complain about that light in the Labour Ward."

The Garrison P.A.D. officer cleared his throat for a second time. "It should have been——" but for a second time he was unable to . finish his protest. The dignified and efficient Mackenzie suddenly exploded quite as violently as the bombs had been exploding a short while ago.

"God Almighty, Dillon! Are you telling me that man is still nattering on about that light? Does he know it was in the Labour Ward? And if he does will you tell him from me that if he wants the bloody babies delivered in the bloody dark with a tin hat and respirator on at the alert, he can come and deliver them himself! Being only a qualified midwife, I have to see what I'm doing! Can I help it if those stupid Germans knock down my black-out screens with their blast when I'm scrubbed up and holding a baby's head? Ask him that, Dillon! And you can also tell him that while he's been pestering me with his bloody 'phone-calls I've brought three babies into the world, and I've got a mother who's going to leave this world mighty soon if I don't get back to her, and someone doesn't get me an M.O. quickly! For the love of Mike, get those babes back into their cots, and then sit on the 'phone until someone gets me a doctor! If they can't find Major Scott get anyone—even that moron Heller. Isn't he O.M.O. to-night? Where the hell's he got to? Why isn't he here?"

I called quickly, "Sister, Mr Heller is——"

"Don't tell me!" she spat back. "I know. Held up by a road-block or a land-mine or something! He would be. God help us! God help all women when men start playing at soldiers!"

She swept back to the Labour Ward with a swirl of her starched skirts.

140

Mr Heller changed instantly from a harassed O.M.O. into a concerned young doctor. "Who's having trouble, Miss Dillon?"

"Mrs Ellis. Sister says she's going to have a P.P.H."

"Is she?" He shot a look at his companions, then made up his mind. "Excuse me, sir, I must go up. A woman needs transfusing." He went up the stairs three at a time.

His disappearance was followed by utter silence. In the silence I hung my hurricane lamp in its original place on the end of the trolley. The Garrison P.A.D. officer helped me with ostentatious gallantry. "Useful things these, aren't they, Nurse? What's happened to your basement lights?"

Mackenzie had inspired me. I said coldly I had not the faintest idea.

"Oh? Oh. Oh." They were three quite different sounds. He turned his attention to my babies. "Jolly lot of little fellows you've got here!" The Major managed a positively matey laugh. "Make a good football team, eh?"

His charm rolled off me. I was on Mackenzie's side, and on a corner of her soap-box. I said my babies would make a rotten football team, as there were only nine on the trolley, four of whom were girls.

"Really?" He cleared his throat again for want of inspiration, then turned on the R.S.M. "Well, Sar'nt-Major, what are we waiting for, eh? I've got work to do, man! Can't hang around here all night delaying this young lady at her excellent work. Expect you've had a hard night, eh, Nurse?"

I said, "Yes. It has been busy."

The R.S.M. was magnificently phlegmatic. "I'll get that screen replaced immediately, sir."

"See you do, Sar'nt-Major! I don't want these good ladies to be worried again in this fashion!"

"Yes, sir! Certainly, sir!" The R.S.M. clicked his heels, then stood aside to let me proceed with my trolley. As I did so the lamp illuminated his impassive face. The left side of his face was away from the Garrison P.A.D. officer and his two attendants. The R.S.M. murmured, "Good night, Miss Dillon," and slowly lowered and raised his left eyelid.

The Major was not to be outdone. "Ah, Miss Dillon, is it? Any relation to my good friend Paul Dillon in the 17/21st?"

"None at all, I'm afraid. Neither of my brothers are in the Army." I was too peeved to explain more; I hoped he would assume both were conscientious objectors.

Apparently he did. He coughed and muttered something about lots of fine chaps still being tied up in Civvy Street. "I know we mustn't keep you down here with your precious cargo. Good night, Miss Dillon."

"Good morning," I returned frigidly, and stalked on towards the lift with my trolley.

Major Scott was racing up the stairs when I reached the top floor. He stopped when he saw me. "I hear Sister's wanting me, Nurse?"

"Yes, please. For Mrs Ellis——"

Mackenzie came out of the ward as I spoke. "Sorry to have to get you back, sir. I'm glad you've come. Mrs Ellis is having a P.P.H. Mr Heller's doing a cut-down."

Major Scott removed his tin hat and draped it over the end of the banister. "How much has she lost, Sister?"

Mackenzie said evenly, "I should say four. Might be more. She hasn't stopped properly yet."

"How much of her group have we got?"

"Six pints."

He had removed his jacket and was rolling up his shirt-sleeves now. "Child all right?"

"Perfect. A girl."

"Good." He yawned. "That's half our battle won already. Right, Sister, let's go and see her. Sorry I couldn't come before. I was held up in the theatre. Gervase Gill cut his right hand—flying glass or something—and I had to take over for him."

They went into the ward then. I closed the nursery door and tucked down my babies, feeling no longer tired or peeved; I felt only very thoughtful. When the nursery was tidy again I stood for quite a long time looking round at the babies I had brought back from the shelter, and then I drifted over to the white-screened corner by the radiator and looked at the three babies I had seen born that night. Mackenzie must have carried their cots from their mothers' bedsides after the all-clear. The two little boys were asleep, Rose Ellis was awake. One of her minute hands had escaped from her shawl and was pressed like a small, fat starfish against her round cheek. She blinked up at me with wide, unfocusing eyes that looked incredibly wise. I touched her hand with my little finger. "You're much too fat to be new," I said aloud. "You ought to have red skinny hands like the others. I think you're a fraud, baby. I think you've been here before. You look as if you know all the answers. I wish I knew a few of them."

"What are your questions?" Mackenzie had come in from the Labour Ward. She did not look surprised to hear me talking to the baby, because both she and I often talked to the babies when we thought ourselves alone.

I turned to her. "I was thinking about the raid, Sister. All the noise and the mess and people killing each other—and Mrs Ellis hæmorrhaging—and wondering why?"

She shrugged. "You never want to waste time wondering why

142

about anything. Leave silly questions to silly people who have nothing better to do than ask them. Certainly you must never stop to ask why in any hospital, no one can answer you—and what does the why matter? What does matter is the job in hand. Which is why I'm in here. Will you make some tea for Mrs Ellis and the two men? Bring it up to this floor, and I'll serve it."

"Yes, Sister. How is Mrs Ellis?"

Her eyes smiled over her mask. "It looks as if she's going to do. And don't ask me why, because I don't know. According to all the books she should have died a couple of hours ago. I don't know why she didn't, either. Now get on and get that tea. The poor woman needs it."

While I made the tea I thought over what Mackenzie had said. She might not know why Mrs Ellis was still alive; I did. I had never read a midder text-book, but I knew I was right. Mrs Ellis was alive because Mackenzie had kept her alive. It was as simple as that. I thought about Best and her Mrs Sinclair. Mrs Sinclair had managed to survive that second raid. I had not read any books on cardiac deseases either, but I knew enough from remembering what my father used to say about his heart patients to know how people who have had one coronary thrombosis are well advised to avoid any form of shock. Possibly, according to the books, Mrs Sinclair should also have died a couple of hours ago. She had not died; in fact, Best had told me, when she came down to the shelter to collect her women after the last all-clear, that her patient "wasn't doing too badly at all. She's been marvellous, Dillon. She just hung on to my hand and never turned a hair."

I wondered how many hairs Mrs Sinclair would have turned had she not had Best's hand to hang on to?

On my way back upstairs with the tea-tray I noticed the grey early-morning light filtering through the cracks in the stair-well black-out. It was as well the stairs were not lighted at night, or that P.A.D. major would have been up the wall about the stair windows too. Having delivered the tray to Mackenzie, I began removing the corridor black-out. It was quite light outside; I looked at the dawn and the camp dispassionately. I felt as if I had no part in either, I was a spectator, a killer of cockroaches, a maker of tea, a lighter of wet wood fires, an un-skilled amateur among skilled professionals, doomed to a life-time of taking down black-outs—if the War lasted my lifetime. Or my lifetime lasted the War? Physical weariness and lack of sleep combined to make me light-headed and vague. I should have been preparing the babies' baths; laying out clean woolly clothes and napkins; switching on sterilizers and teat saucepans. Instead I remained by one open top-storey window and looked

143

out at the camp. I did not see the camp; I saw suddenly Joe's face in memory; I heard him ask scornfully, "Why not learn to do the job properly?"

Joe. I grinned foolishly. There were a lot of 'why's' I wanted to ask about Joe. There were also a lot of things I wanted to tell him. One of those things was that this morning, making tea just before dawn, I had discovered myself at a personal cross-road, and now that it was dawn I saw quite clearly which way I must walk.

9

I KNOW WHERE I'M GOING

I RANG up Mary after breakfast next morning. She was too busy to talk to me. Sergeant Stevens, who answered my call, said the Stables was in the process of being emptied of A.T.S. and filled with semi-convalescent soldiers from the main hospital. "These men are to be moved out to-morrow. We're going to be a Casualty Clearing annexe. We've got two Sisters down here already, and Mrs Frantly-Gibbs said I was to tell you her reign is over, and she's very pleased. She says she'll drop in at the night house to see you as soon as she gets an evening off. She says she'll make it evening, not to disturb your sleep."

"She won't do that, Sarge. I've lost the knack of sleeping by day. Thanks for the message. Give her my love and tell her to ring me at Families to-night, if she can. Oh, yes. Tell her something else. Tell her I saw three babies being born last night."

"You did?" Sergeant Stevens clucked disapprovingly. "Who'd be a nurse! What—was it like, Nurse Dillon?"

I hesitated. "Messy—and fantastic. One moment there was one person there—and then the next there were two. And, Sarge, the babies are sheer heaven! They shout their heads off and look frightfully wise. Like little old men."

"It's a wonder you could hear them shout with all the noise that was going on last night."

"They drowned the noise. We forgot the raid was going on."

"Come, come, Nurse! You don't expect me to believe that? No one could have forgotten that shocking row last night. I suppose you felt rather out of it in your quiet little Families hospital? I expect you were quite glad to have those three babies to give you and the Sisters something to do."

I did not argue with her. There was no point. "I expect we were. Thanks, Sarge, for giving me the message. Give my love to Merrick and Blakney." I rang off and made a face at the receiver. I was not surprised by her attitude because my fellow-V.A.D.'s at breakfast had had the same attitude. They had all commiserated with my spending such an exciting night in an unexciting backwater.

"I bet," they said, "you were aching to come over and join us. We were admitting all night, and some of the men are in a pretty bad way, but not as bad as that first afternoon raid, as everyone's now much more sensible about taking cover fast."

They also said that on one occasion the rumour that Families had had a direct hit had shot round the main hospital. "Did you realize you had a couple of very near misses, Clare?"

"Strangely enough, my loves," I retorted bitterly, "we weren't sleeping all that heavily in our quiet backwater. We did just hear a faint sound of a bomb falling in our back yard."

The post was late that morning, but it was worth waiting for as far as I was concerned. My mother's letter enclosed one from Luke, who was now back at sea, and I had one from Charles. I went out into the garden of the day Mess to read them; we took breakfast and supper in that Mess, the night house having no dining-room. We had two suppers on night duty; one at seven-thirty and another at any time in the middle of the night. From force of habit I drifted through the Drawing-room and out of one of the windows. I was surprised to see how many strange photographs now stood on the orange-boxes in that room; the V.A.D. staff was changing constantly, as more girls were being called up and others being transferred to hospitals farther inland. At breakfast the girls had been full of the rumour that the whole hospital was shortly going to be closed as a base hospital and kept open only as a C.C.S. "The camp's getting too hot for the sick, Dillon. Night Sister was saying that if we have any more nights like last night she's certain the G.O.C. will order us all out. She thinks they'll keep a skeleton trained staff here to cope with casualties, and bung us all inland."

I thought about the rumours as I opened my letters. I thought about them with detachment; they did not seem to concern me at all. The three letters from my family only added to my sense of detachment. I dropped them in my lap and gazed at the empty tennis-courts and thought how impossible it was to believe that my mother or the boys really existed. They had become vague figures in my mind, far more vague than my father, even though he was dead and they were living. At least, as far as I knew, they were still living. I took up the letters again; Charles wrote: "I had a charming letter from Great-Aunt Charlotte last week. The old girl seems in great form and wants me to visit her some time. I think the prospect might be amusing." His letter told me he was in Egypt and enjoying life, since in the private code of likely theatres of war we had worked out before he sailed, Great-Aunt Charlotte stood for Egypt. Reading between the lines in Luke's letter, it was obvious that he was convoying in the Atlantic. I gathered this because he wrote, "The chaps are much amused with my eyelash-curlers. Tell Clare I'll deliver them on my next leave home." Those eyelash-curlers were an American product I had once seen in a glossy American magazine, and Luke had promised to buy me some if he ever reached the States. That message meant he must be on his way back.

I might have been convinced of my mother's existence had she not lived on the south-east coast. Those bombers that attacked us last night must almost certainly have come in from the south-east. She could not know that we had been their target, so she could not know how close had been the odds last night against my being alive this morning. And I could not be sure, until the day was over, if she was alive this morning. There was, I discovered, a saturation point to anxiety. You had to reach that point and pass beyond it to retain your sanity. Before Dunkirk I had been in a flat spin with worrying over Charles; then I discovered that I had been worrying about the wrong person. Possibly, even had my father not been killed, I would have grown detached; it was my only defence, and not only mine, but the defence of everyone else. There was now no future in worry, because there was now no future over which to worry. To-day I was alive; to-morrow I might be dead. The prospect did not frighten me; it was just something that was on the cards for everyone. Perhaps if I had not been so perpetually tired I might have been frightened. I was far too weary to bother with fear—death at least would be restful, and mean one could sleep.

My head jerked forward sharply. It was warm in the garden, so I lay back on the grass and decided to snooze for a little while before I went back to the night house. I thought of Joe as I relaxed; I would much rather not die; I wanted to see Joe again. There was so much I had to tell him. So much; and I still did not know where he was. Sleep was drugging my mind and the sun above was warming my body. I yawned. I would think about it all later. Not now.

Two hours later Miss Moreby-Aspin woke me by shaking me firmly, "Dillon, m'dear. You ought to be in bed, child. You can't sleep out here. There's a raid going on. Come in at once. You'll have to wait until the all-clear and then cycle to the night house quickly."

I followed her indoors with my eyes half shut. Somewhere far off I heard gunfire and the sound of aeroplanes. I was not interested in any raid. I was off duty, and it was no concern of mine. I sat on one of the chairs in the sitting-room and went back to sleep. Again I was shaken to temporary wakefulness. "Dillon, m'dear. Where's your tin hat? And where is your respirator? Get both at once!"

"Sorry, Madam." I did as she said, then, having collected both from the hall, looked round for the nearest seat. There was a wooden high-backed bench in the hall. I lay full length on it, hanging my feet over the end; I sat my respirator on my chest, put the wretched tin hat on my head, and fell asleep again. I slept undisturbed until lunch-time as Madam was too occupied to notice me. Polly, the Home V.A.D., woke me with a cup of tea.

"Polly, you are an angel! Thank you so much." I lifted my feet, and she sat down beside me.

"What it is to be young, Dillon! How you can possibly sleep upon this hard bench with the noise we've had I cannot imagine."

I drank the scalding tea gratefully. "Was it a very rowdy raid?"

"Nothing like last night, but more exciting to watch. They stopped the ack-ack, as we had dog-fights going on overhead. Don't tell Madam I was watching, but really it was thrilling. I've never seen 'planes fighting before. The Spits were marvellous. They were here, there, and everywhere."

"The boys from Upper Weigh?"

"I expect so. Seems as if we've got a R.A.F. after all. You should have seen them!"

"No doubt I will some other time." I stretched my arms. "Your tea's put new life into me, Polly. I'd better make tracks for the night house while this quiet lasts."

"Don't fall asleep on your bike. You don't look awake to me yet. And don't let Madam see you. Your apron's a wreck, and your cap looks as if you've been through a bush backwards."

I smoothed my apron skirt ineffectively, removed my cap, combed my hair, and put on my tin hat. "If anyone stops me I'll say this is the new outdoor uniform for V.A.D.'s. So long as I don't run into Madam, I'll get away with it."

Mary rang me in Families that night. We could only talk for a few minutes because of an alert that proved to be a false alarm, and after that telephone call it was over a week before I saw her again. She came round to my room one evening to tell me she had had no success at all with her father-in-law.

"And to crown it, I've been posted. I'm going to the Rangmere C.C.S."

I thanked her for her help. "I hate your going. The old firm's breaking up."

"You've not been posted, have you, Clare?"

"No, but I'm not staying. I'm going to remuster, like Agatha. I think she's done the right thing. I'm going to apply to Matthew and Mark's."

"Clare—are you serious?" She sat on my bed. "What about Joe?"

"What about him?" I looked at her. "He's still lost in thin air. And I'm still busy asking questions about him, but no one's got the time to find out the answers for me. There's another thing——" I told her my thoughts in the nursery the night before last. "I think it's time I did something about it."

"It's a big step," she said. "Real nursing can hardly be called a game."

"And is this?"

She sighed. "No. I see your point. Why Matthew and Mark's? Because of your father? Because of Agatha? Or Thanet and Mackenzie? It's considered the strictest training school, Clare. They take life very seriously in that hospital, I've heard."

"I think that's a good thing. If Thanet and Mackenzie are typical examples of what they turn out I think Matthew and Mark's must know what it's doing. If they accept me I'll be very bucked. Mary—I'm sick of fumbling in the dark. I'm sick of not knowing what to do—apart from cleaning. Boy, can I clean! But I want to know more than how to clean. I like this job, I like nursing, and I want to learn how to do it. I don't want to spend the War fiddling round from post to post, and, as Agatha said, getting no place fast. If I'm going to nurse I'll go the whole hog, and become an S.R.N., and an S.C.M. if necessary."

"And would all this be to help you get Joe out of your system?" she asked quietly. "You're choosing a pretty drastic method."

I said, "I don't want him out of my system. The way I feel now he'll never be out of my system. If he really feels the same about me I can take that. I don't say I'll enjoy waiting years and years—if we have got years and years in which to wait."

"You think he'll recover sooner?"

"I think we may both be blown to Kingdom Come before the years have passed. But we might not be. People do survive wars. We've survived most of this summer; why shouldn't we survive the rest? If we don't—well—at least there's no harm in trying."

She said, "Clare, you sound more assured than I have ever heard you sound. You're talking like an adult."

"I'm that all right." I smiled at her. "You've always said we were all growing up too fast. I'm a big girl now, love. I have looked on death and birth and cockroaches. And the cockroaches frighten me much more than the other two."

She walked to the dormer window. "The leaves are turning early this year. It must be the lack of rain. Summer's not over yet."

"It can't last much longer. It's September already."

She peered downward. "What are all those soldiers doing in your garden?"

"Are they lying on their stomachs and crawling about on their elbows?" I asked, without getting up.

"Yes. How did you know that?"

"Because they are always doing it these days. It's called deploying. I don't know why they have to deploy round our house; they just do. Doesn't David deploy?"

"If he does he hasn't told me."

"How is David?"

"Fine. Far as I know. Thanks." She turned round. "He's got a Staff job now. In Cairo, from what I make out from his letters." She grinned affectionately. "Imagine poor darling David on the Staff. Heaven help the Army now!"

I said I was delighted he was on the Staff. "He'll probably end this war as Major-General. You wait and see."

Agnes banged on my door. "You up, ducks? Gentleman wanting to talk to you on the telephone downstairs. Gentleman from your home. A Dr Anthony, he says he is." I must have changed colour, because she added quickly and kindly, "You don't need to fret, dear. The gentleman said to tell you it wasn't bad news about your mum. He just wants to talk to you."

I stared at Mary. "It's Uncle Michael." I leapt out of bed and ran downstairs in my pyjamas.

Uncle Michael's voice sounded as clearly as if he were in the camp. "That you, Clare? Sorry to get you out of bed, lass, but I've news for you. Your mother's well and sends her love. I'm calling about your letter. This chap Slaney you asked me about. I've found where he's hospitalized."

"Uncle Michael—you're wonderful! How did you find out?"

"Quite easily, lass. If you were so bothered why didn't you ask me before? I dropped a line to Tom Lomax. He was in your father's year at Matthew and Mark's. I explained who I was and why I was asking, and I had a short note from him to-day. This fellow Slaney is in one of the civilian sanatoria. It's roughly a hundred and ten miles from you. Here's the address. . . ."

"There! Uncle, don't I know it? Didn't you and Father go fishing there sometimes?"

"In that direction. This place is in the hills above the river. It's reasonably high for England. Good spot. Good sanatorium. That all you wanted to know?"

I said slowly, "I suppose you can't find out how badly he's got it? How—long—and so on?"

"Clare!" he laughed. "Are you asking me to divulge a professional confidence?"

"Yes, Uncle."

"That's what I thought you were doing. Well. I'll see what I can do. I didn't ask Lomax, naturally, but I rang up the place for you to discover who is the Medical Superintendent. It's a man called MacArthur. D. B. MacArthur. I used to know a Dennis MacArthur who was reading medicine at Cambridge. Might be the same man. I left my name and qualifications and asked him to call me back. If he is the man I know he may be able to help. If not, at a pinch I can tackle Lomax again. He seemed to remember your father very well, and said some very pleasant things about him in his note. I'll show it to you when you next have leave. Any idea when that's to be?"

"Not off-hand. I might be able to wangle a forty-eight on top of my nights off when I finish this spell."

"But you'll want to use some of that visiting the sick?"

"Yes, I will. Thank you," I said gratefully, "for being so understanding. Will you explain to Mother?"

"I will. She knows most of this already. You don't mind that?"

"Of course not. Listen, Uncle, will you tell her something else?" I told him my ideas about training. "Do you think it a good idea?"

"I think it the best idea you've had in your life. You go ahead, lass, and if you want to use my name as a reference use it any time you like." He chuckled deeply. "As I'm your mother's brother, we've got different surnames, so they won't twig our relationship. But to be serious, if you really need a string to pull to get you in I'm fairly sure Lomax would pull it for you. He said he thought your father one of the best men and soundest physicians he had ever met. That's something to be proud of, Clare. Lomax is considered an authority on medicine. So you let me know what you want me to do—and when you see this fellow Slaney you can tell him from me that he may as well give in gracefully. Or did he ask you to marry him before he knew what he had got?"

"No. Nothing like that."

"You mean you two are not unofficially engaged?"

"No, Uncle. We're not. Only——"

"Only you feel the time has come to put that little matter right?"

"Well—yes. Sort of."

"You'll do it," he said cheerfully, "you'll do it. I suppose you feel you may as well train during the waiting years and then get married?"

"Something like that."

"Then the poor fellow has as much chance of stopping you as of holding up a panzer division single-handed. I know you, lass, once you make up your mind. You're like your father. You've a grip like the teeth of a bulldog. I—er—presume he's a decent fellow?"

I said, "Yes. Yes. He's decent. He's the son of the *Survey of British Birds*."

"That Slaney? Your father would have been interested to know that. Would your father have liked him?"

151

I hesitated. "As he was when I first met him—no. Then he changed; he changed a lot this summer. I think Father would have liked him as he was when we were last together."

"Well," said my Uncle Michael, "we've all been young fools in our time. Your particular generation have undoubtedly been extraordinarily foolish, possibly because you had so little time for folly. I cannot call any of you foolish now. Look after yourself, lass. Your mother worries about you a lot. Always let me know if there is anything I can do for you."

I rushed up to Mary as if I were walking on air. "He was so sweet, Mary! I don't know what's come over him. He never had much time for girls when we were growing up. He always made a fuss of the boys. Not me."

"Has he any children of his own?"

"He's never married."

"Maybe he regrets that now. And maybe he's touched that you wrote to him for help. People love being asked for their help. It makes them feel wanted."

"Perhaps that's it. Oh, Mary!" I swung her round. "Isn't life glorious! I can go and see Joe!"

She smiled. "There's just the little question of leave, dear! And the other little matter of the War."

"To hell with the War! It's growing like the weather and becoming a bore! I refuse to let it worry me any more. I've got far too much to think of. And first I've got to think what reason I can give Madam to persuade her that I must have at least a thirty-six. Or do you think I can travel two hundred and twenty miles in a twenty-four? I'm not bothered about missing sleep; but the raids or the invasion business might hold up the trains."

She lay back on my bed and rocked with laughter. "They might, dear," she spluttered, "but you wouldn't let them stop you. You've got a bike."

"Mary, that part of the world's awfully hilly. I don't think I could ride all——" I realized that she was laughing at me, and I laughed with her. "All right. I'll try for a forty-eight and work down. And if she doesn't give me anything I'll go A.W.O.L. and be the first V.A.D. in history to be put on a charge. The War will have to get on without me just long enough for me to go and visit Joe. I refuse to waste time in getting it, either. I've wasted quite enough as it is."

She was still laughing. "Clare! Being in love certainly gives you the strength of ten! I've never known you so determined."

"It's not that." I broke off. "Perhaps it is. But—what has suddenly got me, Mary, is the thought that there may not be any time left. Those idiots have got the range of this camp now and are bound to keep on with their raids. If some miserable Jerry gets a direct hit on Families to-night I shall be absolutely livid! And it's all so pointless—such a waste of bombs." I brushed my hair violently to let off steam. "What good can it do them to blow up a collection of sick and newly delivered mothers and a nursery of new-born babies?"

She stopped laughing. "All obvious cracks aside, dear, if they do blow up Families they'll blow up more than they're bargaining for. You, being buried among the women and kids, can't know the feeling that's flying round about Families having such a close shave last week. If one of those bombers had crash-landed in the camp that night a regiment of M.P.'s wouldn't have saved the crews from lynching." She looked at me soberly. "I've never known the troops in such an ugly mood before. Ugly is the only word for it. Did you realize that night how close you girls were to the Pearly Gates?"

"No. I didn't realize until I went on the following night and saw how near the craters were to our building. I was too tired to notice anything properly on the morning after that bad raid, I was upset about Joe, fed up with cockroaches, and plain blue. I didn't have time to take it in or to be frightened during the raid." I explained in detail why. "The War just became something tedious in the background."

She said she supposed she could understand that. "I think they ought to shift out all those women and babies, all the same."

"The sick women were going to-day—I haven't a notion to where. The midder floor is moving to the ground floor and staying open for the time being, and there was some talk of making a nursery out of the shelter. I think it'll remain talk because of the business of fresh air; there's not enough down there for new-born babies, if they're going to stay-put day in and day out. Mackenzie told us the G.O.C. himself went round Families yesterday and talked with the women." I told her about the faulty Labour Ward black-out. "I wonder if the G.O.C. heard the hell one of his stooges gave us that night? In retrospect, I can't help feeling sorry for that wretched major. He was only doing his job—and he got a ghastly time from us. I wish you could have heard Mackenzie! She's normally civility itself with the men—and she let her hair down with a wham!" I noticed the time, and began to dress hastily. "Mary, if you don't mind, I'm going to fly. I want to see Madam before we have supper. I know I won't get that forty-eight unless I create like mad, so the sooner I start creating the better."

Mary cycled to the day Mess with me. "Good luck with your creating, dear. If Madam fails you try Matron; if Matron's no good go and see the C.O."

I got off my bicycle. "Do you think I'll have to go as high as that?"

153

"Possibly." She smiled. "If he turns you down give me a shout. I was at school with the G.O.C.'s wife. She's a nice woman. She might be able to get you an interview with him, and as one of the little heroines from Families"—she bowed to me as she rode in a circle—"I'm sure you rate at least a forty-eight from him."

"Mary, you're an angel! Thank goodness for your strings. I'll shout for you all right, if need be. First, I'd better tackle Madam. What do you think she'll say? That I'm a rat to think of leaving the sinking ship even for a forty-eight?"

"Beat her to it with all the world loving a lover." She made another circle round me. "Clinch it with discretion being the better part of valour. Use the lot on her, dear. You've always been splendid at platitudes. And, Clare—good luck for to-night. If those idiots, as you call them, drop a direct hit on Families to-night I shall be absolutely—livid, too. And so will poor Joe."

"Him! Huh! Mary, do get off—you're making me dizzy. I want to ask you something."

She stopped her bicycle and came towards me pushing it. "What now? I thought you were in a hurry?"

"I am. But I want to know something, and you are always right. Tell me, please. Do you honestly think he's in love with me? Or do you think this is all something I've worked up in my imagination? Tell me," I insisted, "please?"

She did not answer for a few moments. "If I tell you what I honestly think is the truth, will you promise to do something for me?"

I nodded. "It's a deal."

"Right. I think," she said thoughtfully, "that Joe does love you. I think he loves you so much that he would rather hurt himself than hurt you. You may think that kind of love is common, Clare. I assure you it isn't. This is what I want you to do for me. It isn't much. I just want you to remember when you see Joe what you've just been saying about time running short. And I want you to forget all the rubbish you've ever been taught about suitable behaviour for young ladies and waiting for the man to speak first and so on. To-morrow may be another day; let's hope it is; we'd be fools to bank on it. I'm pretty certain you'll be sensible about this, without my good advice, but I feel I'd like to hand it on, all the same. Now do hurry in, dear, or you may miss Madam."

Miss Moreby-Aspin was obviously disturbed by my request. "I would like to help you, Dillon, m'dear, but I must remind you there is a war on. We need all hands to the pump. Matron's very pressed for time. I doubt if she can spare you an interview."

I said, "Will you ask her, Madam? Or shall I?"

She clicked her teeth. "I'll put in a word when I can, m'dear.

Matron's a busy woman. She doesn't spare herself. Frankly, I do not see how she can spare you at this juncture. I think you would be wise to wait until you come off nights."

There was no question of my being able to see Matron that night; I appreciated that, and went on duty in a slightly mutinous frame of mind. I found Families a changed place. Miss Best and her patients had vanished; Mackenzie and I were alone with the maternity patients and the babies who were now all on the ground floor. We took our supper in the kitchen despite the cockroaches, as the office was officially out of bounds. Over supper I asked Mackenzie if she thought I could persuade Matron at least to see me.

"She can't not see you." She swept three cockroaches off the table as she spoke. "No matron can refuse to see one of her nurses with a genuine reason for an interview. You'll just have to by-pass your Commandant and go straight to Matron's office in the morning and demand an interview. I'm quite sure she won't refuse your interview or request if she can possibly grant it. Matron only looks terrifying; she's tolerably human underneath. Your Commandant may be a little scared of her; she possibly hasn't trained, and isn't used to matrons. Sit still." She brushed an insect from my cap. "Inquisitive little horrors, aren't they? That chap"—she nodded amicably at the fallen cockroach, who was now lying on his back waving his legs—"was admiring your red cross."

I shuddered. "Sister, how can you stand them?"

"I can't. I'm terrified of them," she added calmly. "I just force myself to be academic about them as I've got to live with them. It doesn't stop my being terrified, but it does help me maintain some self-respect. It's a mistake to let that go. Asking for trouble."

"Did you," I asked curiously, "learn that sort of thing for yourself, or were you taught it when you were training?"

"Probably a bit of both. In a good training school they bring that kind of thing out. Why?"

I told her that I was seriously considering training as a nurse.

She said, "I've been wondering why you haven't done that before. Of course you must go and train. And of course you must go to Matthew and Mark's."

I smiled at her tone. "I had intended applying there. You think it the best hospital, Sister?"

She smiled back. "My good girl, it is the only hospital. There are others—I believe. To a Matthew and Mark's nurse, the others exist in the Dark Ages." She laughed with me. "I appreciate how I must sound, but I can't help it. I love my hospital, Dillon; I hope one day you'll love it too." She glanced at her watch. "Fifteen minutes before we need start work, so let's

155

rough out your letter of application now. I'll tell you what to say. Then if there's time later—Jerry permitting—you can copy it out neatly. Oh, get out of the way, you revolting creatures!" More cockroaches were swept to the floor. "Pass me my case. I've got some paper in there—oh, no!" The alert instead of the cockroaches had upset her this time. "Never mind. We'll write it after the all-clear. At least we've finished our supper. Jerry's getting positively considerate."

I did not have to confront either the C.O. or the G.O.C. with my demand for forty-eight hours' leave. Matron, as Mackenzie anticipated, granted me an interview on request.

When I had explained why I had asked to see her she said, "You have had no nights off duty during your period in the Families Hospital, Miss Dillon?"

"No, Matron."

"And you have never requested compassionate leave previously? The occasion of your father's death does not concern us now. Leave was granted you then without your requesting it. You have had no other request?"

"No, Matron."

She considered me, then consulted a list on her desk. "You have three nights owing to you at this moment. One for each week you have worked on night duty. In two days' time you will have completed your fourth week. Normally you would then be returning to day duty, but under present circumstances, as you are acquainted with the work in Families, I would like you to continue there until we are able to transfer all our remaining maternity cases. We are hoping to have that scheme completed in another two weeks." My hopes, which had soared, now fell as quickly. Two weeks. Anything could happen in two weeks. She might as well have talked of two hundred weeks, or two hundred years.

She looked up at me keenly. "Are you sleeping well, Miss Dillon?"

I hesitated, wondering even if she was being ironical. "I'm sorry, Matron? I'm afraid I don't quite understand?"

"I asked if you were sleeping well, Miss Dillon. In the daytime? You appear very tired. Are you finding it difficult to train yourself to sleep by day?"

"A little difficult, Matron," was all I dared admit. I wondered if the stout and faintly formidable lady with rows of medal ribbons who was regarding me shrewdly realized I had just made the understatement of the year.

Apparently she did. "I well remember the trouble I had with my sleep when I was a probationer. I was in my third year before I was able to sleep as well by day as by night. Consequently, I can appreciate how exhausting young nurses like yourself do find night duty. Nor do I discount the added strain under which we are all working. I think you will do better work, Miss Dillon, if you have a couple of nights in bed. So," she tapped her desk with the third finger of her right hand, "I am going to allow you to take two nights off duty, starting from to-night. I will speak to Miss Moreby-Aspin about a temporary replacement for you immediately."

I could not believe this was true. "Matron, thank you very much."

"You must understand, Miss Dillon," she said gravely, "that my principal reason for granting you this leave is because I recognize that you need to sleep. As you are on leave, you will naturally be free to leave the hospital and the camp, so long as you return at the appointed time. But remember, I am trusting you to ensure that, wherever you may go, you do have two full nights in bed. I do not wish to hear that you have returned to duty looking as tired as you are this morning."

I cycled back to the day Mess as if I were on a dirt-track. When I arrived I found Madam looking slightly annoyed and Polly beaming. Polly told me Miss Moreby-Aspin had already heard the news and had rung the Company Office about my travel warrant. "She's not annoyed about you. The poor old girl's heartbroken. She's just heard that this place is turning into a C.C.S. and not a base hospital for sure by the end of this month."

"What's going to happen to everyone?"

"Heaven knows. Most of us'll be posted; and this house will close down or be taken over for troops."

"Is Madam going to stay?"

"She doesn't know. That's what's eating her most. Are you going to sleep at all to-day, Dillon?"

"I'll sleep in the train. I'm not going to waste time in bed this morning. I'll be in bed to-night."

"Where are you going? Has your mother evacuated? That why you're going west instead of east?"

"No. She's still on the coast. I'm going to visit a friend." I was not more specific, because I had no idea where I was going to stay, or where I would find the bed in which I had promised Matron to get two good nights' sleep. "I'll go back to the night house now, Polly, and bath and change. By the time I'm back here Madam should have my warrant and pass lined up—I hope."

"She's going up to the office in a few minutes. I've got to go up to the hospital myself; if you like I'll ride up with her and bring yours back. You won't want to go all the way back to the hospital, and if you want to get off this morning you may be held up, as Madam seldom gets back from the office before twelve. With luck I'll be back here at half-past nine."

I had not been able to hug Matron, much as I had wanted to. I could and did hug Polly. "Heaven will reward you, my love, even if I don't. I'll see you then."

I had a third stroke of luck that morning. I was able to hitch a lift in an empty ambulance, and was on the local station platform by five minutes past ten. The R.T.O. looked doubtfully at my warrant. "If you are thinking of going through London you had better think again. There's a four-hour delay on all trains to London. You'll be wiser to go across country. You'll have to change"—he consulted a note-book—"three, possibly four, times. It'll take you five hours—with luck. Be a shockingly boring journey, but the farther west you get the less chance you'll have of being held up by raids."

"Then I'll go west from the start. How long do I have to wait for the first train?"

"That one over there is the one you want. It should have gone half an hour ago, so you may not have too much of a wait here." He opened the door of a first-class carriage. "This is empty. Hop in."

I hesitated. "My warrant's third. Does it matter?"

His smile was weary. "Not in the slightest. This is the last empty carriage. If you had wanted to go via London you would probably have had to ride in the van. There's a war on, you know."

I was too happy and too sleepy to do more than apologize humbly. "I'm so sorry. I forgot. Thank you very much." I sat contentedly in the comfortable, empty compartment, clutched my suitcase on my lap, and settled down to sleep. Then I realized that I might well sleep through my first change. I was fairly sure I was not going to remain alone in the compartment, so I opened my case, took out an envelope and my pen, wrote in large capitals the name of the station at which I had to get out, added beneath it, "Please wake me up," and pinned the note to the turned-up brim of my pork-pie cap. I settled down again and was asleep before the train started, or anyone joined me.

After what seemed like a couple of moments I felt a hand on my shoulder. "Miss. Miss. Wake up." A soldier was bending over me. "Was you wanting to get out here?"

I blinked at him. "What? What time is it? It's still light——" Then I remembered where I was. "Thanks awfully." I jumped up and dropped my suitcase. The soldier picked it up and followed me out on to the platform.

"Where you going now, miss?"

I told him. "I hope it's one of the trains in now. I'll go and find an R.T.O. and ask."

He had spotted a couple of railway policemen. "That corporal over there might know, miss. You sure you're awake? Then I'd best leave you. Going on in the other, I am." He vanished before I could thank him for his kindness.

The railway policeman put me in a third-class carriage. "Sorry, miss, no seats left in the first. It's a bit of a crush in here"—he scowled at the many occupants of the carriage until they made room for me—"but be better than standing."

I was pleased to be in a crowd. It would save me writing another label. I asked if anyone was going to my next destination. A faintly gloomy soldier nodded. "I'm changing there, miss Cruel dump it is."

I asked if he would mind waking me. He looked even more gloomy. "I was thinking of having a kip myself, miss."

"Then we'll both kip." I took the now crumpled label from my pocket, altered the station name, added, "Soldier opposite too, please," and pinned it once more to my cap. The men watched me seriously. A man in the far corner said he reckoned that wasn't a bad plan and wrote a label for himself. He stuck it in his shoulder-strap, then folded his arms and closed his eyes.

When I arrived at the West Country market town that was my final destination my label had been altered four times and I was feeling very refreshed after nearly five and a half hours' sleep. I could not understand why I could sleep so well sitting upright in a crowded, moving train, and not at all in my bed in my room, but I did not stop to worry on the subject. I was only too pleased to have had some sleep, and to have arrived with at least four more hours of daylight ahead in which to find somewhere to spend the next two nights. I did not think about seeing Joe in the immediate future at all; I did not dare think about him. I was going to face that problem only when I came to it. First I wanted to wash and tidy myself, have a cup of tea, and then find a room.

I asked the girl at the railway buffet counter about hotels. "Any chance of getting a room?"

"Not a hope, dear," she said cheerfully. "There's not a room in the town. Filled with evacuees we are. Everything's taken."

"Aren't there any boarding-houses? Commercial hotels?" She was shaking her head all the time, so I asked desperately, "There must be somewhere I can spend the night? What do I do?"

She reached for the chained teaspoon. "Couldn't say." She had lost interest in my problems. She strolled away, humming *A Nightingale sang in Berkeley Square*. She hummed flat, killing the pleasant melody.

I carried my saucerless cup over to one of the tables. Two A.T.S. in uniform smiled at me, so I moved to their table. "Can you girls tell me how I can find a room—or even a bed—for a couple of nights?"

The A.T.S. girls were far more helpful than the buffet lady. "Wonder if they've got any Salvation Army here? If not, try the Y.W. There must be a Y.W. somewhere. They'll fix you up with something, as you're in uniform. The Y.W. are ever so good about fixing us up. They're clean, too. But you'll have to be in on time. They don't like you coming in late."

"I'll be in early." I swallowed my tea. "Thanks, girls. You've given me a lot of good ideas. Now I come to think of it, there's a Y.W. sign up in the Ladies' Room. I'll go and look at it for the address."

The elderly lady in charge of the small branch of the Young Women's Christian Association looked harassed by my request. "We'll certainly fit you in, my dear, if you can't find any other room. You'll have to share with six others."

I smiled. "I've been used to sharing with twenty. That won't bother me at all." I asked her about Joe's sanatorium. "Do you know how I can get there?"

She sighed. "Oh, dear me. I don't. It's a good walk—at least five miles—and the bus only goes out there twice a day now. I doubt whether you'll be able to get a taxi—even could you afford it. Taxis are very expensive now, and very rare."

"Five miles." I answered her sigh with another. "How I wish I had brought my bike. I can't say I feel much like the walk, but if there is no other way of getting there I'll have to walk."

"Have you had a very long journey?" she asked sympathetically.

"Moderately long. I'm on night duty, which is why I'm not feeling exactly like walking. But I've come all this way to visit someone there, and now I'm here I'm going to see him. May I leave my case and have a wash before I go?"

"I'll just give you a receipt for your case." She clucked over her receipt-book. "I don't like your having to walk there and back. Did you say you rode a bicycle? Wait one moment." She disappeared into a back room, and came back with another, younger woman. "Miss Aspey, this is the young girl who wants to get to the sanatorium. She is coming back here to-night."

Miss Aspey was about Mary's age. She looked me over. "You can borrow my bike if you like—so long as you bring it back safely."

"May I? Thank you so much. I'll be very careful with it."

She grinned. "It's not much of a machine, I'm afraid. It belonged to my mother. But it goes. It'll be better than walking. Now, do you know how to get to the sanatorium? And have you got permission to visit someone there? They're fairly sticky about visitors."

I said I did not know the way and had not got permission.

160

That snag had not occurred to me. I refused to let it worry me now.

Miss Aspey said, "I suppose the person you are visiting had told them you are coming?"

"Probably," I lied. I did not dare admit that I had not warned Joe of my arrival, because I suspected he might refuse to see me. I had concentrated all my energy on getting here. I was going to wait until I reached the sanatorium before I began flapping about what to do next.

10

A HOSPITAL ON A HILL

THE porter in the glass-fronted lodge was polite but firm. "It's not a visiting day, miss. Is Dr Slaney expecting you? I've had no message from Sister Franks."

"He's not expecting me, but——"

He closed the large admission book in front of him. "I can't let you in without permission, miss. Would you like me to have a word with the ward Sister?"

I hesitated, then made up my mind. "Is Dr MacArthur free?"

"The Superintendent, miss?" His tone altered slightly. "You—would be a friend of the Superintendent, miss?"

"I'm the niece of a friend of his." I did not know if this was true or not, as I had not heard from Uncle Michael since that telephone call, but, having decided to use his name, I was determined to plug it. "My uncle is a Dr Anthony. Dr M. H. Anthony. Could you ask Dr MacArthur if he could see me?"

He bounced out of his lodge and asked me to take a seat in the hall. "Won't keep you long, miss, I'm sure." He grew more effusive with every passing second. "I'll put a call through to the Superintendent right away. Miss Anthony, is it?"

"No—Miss Dillon. My uncle is Dr Anthony. Thank you."

Ten minutes later a small, spare man in a long white coat strolled into the entrance hall. He stopped in front of me. "Miss Dillon? I believe you wanted to see me."

I stood up. "Dr Dennis MacArthur?" I was surprised to hear my voice sound steady. I felt extremely unsteady.

He shook his head slightly. "No. My name happens to be Desmond. Why? What's all this about a Dr Aston?"

I said, "Oh, dear. The porter must have misunderstood me. I said Dr Anthony. He's my uncle. I—er—hoped you would know him."

He smoothed his grey, thinning hair. "Why?"

I told him the truth.

His face gave nothing away as he listened. Then he asked, "Why didn't you let Dr Slaney know you were coming?"

I met his eyes. "I'm not sure that he wants to see me."

"I see. And you want to see him now?"

"Yes, please."

He looked at his feet. "How did you get out here? There's no bus at this time of the evening."

"Someone lent me a bicycle."

"Have you friends in the town?"

"No. A woman at the Y.W. lent it to me."

"Y.W.C.A.?"

"Yes."

He smiled faintly. "You said you were on night duty. Did you work last night?"

"Yes." I wished he would make up his mind and stop this cross-examination. If he was not going to let me see Joe this evening I wished he would tell me so at once.

He was not to be hurried. "Have you had any meals to-day?"

"I had breakfast—and some tea at the station."

"Do they feed you at the Y.W.?"

"I don't know. I forgot to ask. I don't think so."

He said, "I see. Well, Miss Dillon, before I let you see Dr Slaney I want to tell you something. This hospital, and other similiar establishments all over the country, is filled to capacity with young men and women who have been as oblivious as you seem to be about the requirements of the human body. Adequate rest and food are not merely the needs of the very young or very old. I do understand that this is a somewhat exceptional circumstance for you, but I make it a point never to allow such behaviour to pass without comment. If you try and run any machine without care it'll break down; the same applies to the human body. If you are in any doubt about the result of constantly over-working and under-feeding I would advise you to take a look round this hospital. And let me remind you," he added soberly, "that nine-tenths of my patients are under the age of thirty. Now, you are not to ride back to your Y.W. to-night before you have had a proper dinner here. If you wish to come out to-morrow—yes, you may—you must take your meals with the nurses. I will mention the subject to Matron. The ward Sister will show you where to go. No, don't thank me, young woman. I'm only doing my job. We do not only aim to cure here; we also aim to prevent." He beckoned the porter. "Davis, take this lady to see Dr Slaney. Tell Sister Franks that Miss Dillon has my permission."

I thanked him warmly, and felt more than a little sick. I followed the porter, wondering if my legs would carry me. My stomach was tying itself in knots, and my mouth was dry, while strange things were happening to my knees.

A tall, dark-haired woman in a Sister's blue dress looked at me curiously as she received the Superintendent's message. "I did not know Dr Slaney was expecting a visitor," she said, with a strong guttural accent. "But if Dr MacArthur gives permission, naturally all is well. You will come with me?"

The ward was on the ground floor, and the whole of one wall

consisted of folding glass screens. I hurried after the ward Sister, who was striding over the polished floor at a tremendous pace, and noticed nothing but that wall of folded screens. I wondered how they managed to black it out at night, or whether they did not bother about black-outs up here. The War seemed to belong to another world; it had no place on this quiet hill. Even below, in the market town, the brief period I had spent looking round the street I wanted had given me the impression that the War was an inconvenience deplored by all, with the possible exception of the shopkeepers, to whom it must have brought extra business. A series of hills separated the town from the sanatorium. I had had to walk uphill a good half of my journey, and been grateful for the respite I got when that borrowed bicycle sailed downhill. My journey had ended on my feet, as the sanatorium was built on the crest of the highest hill. The pine-woods had been cut back to make room for the long, low, sprawling building; the nearest trees seemed to me about five hundred yards from the place, and in the space there was a garden in which most of the flowers were dead.

The Sister turned right at the end of the ward and strode down a small corridor. "The private rooms," she announced over her shoulder. She stopped and rapped at a door marked Number 7. She swept open the door without waiting for any answer. "Dr Slaney. A visitor." She ushered me in, nodded at us both, and with a rustle of her starched skirts swept out.

The small room was full of air, and, like the long ward, possessed only three solid walls. The outside glass partition wall was folded right back and the solitary bed occupying that room had been pulled to the edge of the now non-existent wall and faced the hills and the pine-woods. Joe was reading when Sister opened the door. He twisted his head round when she announced that he had a visitor, but did not put down his book. When she left us his head remained twisted round and his expression changed for the third time. His first glance had been only incurious; then he saw me, and for a fleeting moment his whole face was illuminated, as someone had switched on an electric light behind his eyes; almost immediately that light faded; he smiled a polite little smile.

"Well, now," said Joe, "there can be no doubt about this. Dr Livingstone, I presume?"

"Yes. That's right." I walked to his bedside. "Joe, tell me something. How do they black-out this place? It must be a nightmare to keep all this glass under cover."

"They've got it pretty well taped. If you step back a foot and look up you'll see the technique. Those rolled blinds look thin, but they're quite light-proof. And those clips at the sides behind the folding wall hold the sides intact."

"What happens about air?" I asked.

"We have to get that through the doors at night. If the night Sister's in a good mood—and she generally is—we talk her into letting the night nurse remove our bulbs. Then we have our blinds up again. Not that it would make the slightest difference if we left in our bulbs and left up the blinds."

I looked at him properly for the first time. I noticed that he was looking much more rested than when we had last been together. I had to look away quickly; he was looking at me, too. "Don't you get any raids?"

"Raids? You've no conception, woman, how dangerous it is up here on these hills. There was a bomb—one bomb, I'm telling you—dropped on a barn in a village fourteen miles from us. Or rather, everyone swears blind it was a bomb, but no one actually heard it fall or go off. So we can't afford to take chances, living on the front line as we do. And we really go to town on our raid drill. The place bristles with wardens and chaps blowing whistles. It's big stuff." He closed the book that was now lying face down on his bed, smoothed his top sheet, and faced me. "And now we've had the small talk, let's get down to it, Clare. Just what do you think you are doing here?"

"I've come to see you," I replied obviously, and looked round for a chair and to give myself time to think. "I can't get down to brass tacks on my two feet. As there is no chair, what can I sit on? The end of your bed?"

"No." He removed some books from the lower shelf of his locker. "This thing is a seat." He pushed it away from his bed. "Why not heave it out into the garden? On the path just there. It'll be more pleasant. The sun is still warm."

I leant on the back of the locker. "Joe, I'm going to tell you a story. Once upon a time there was an Acute Medical Block full of soldiers with tubercle. I washed, fed, held those soldiers for two months on days, and one month on nights. They breathed and coughed all over me; generally when I was not wearing a mask. Not once, but many, many times. I must have inhaled millions of their bugs; don't be so fussy about yours. And stop behaving as if I'm a fragile little flower—and as if you've got leprosy. Incidentally, my fathre used to say that even lepers were not nearly so infectious as people have made out for centuries."

He had listened to me with an expressionless face. "End of your story, Clare?" he asked civilly.

"Yes."

"Then take that bastard of a locker out into the garden as I told you and stop arguing. If you don't I'll ring for help and say you're upsetting me. No one's allowed to upset patients here. This is a civvy hospital. I've only to press my bell and they'll

165

fetch the boss to chuck you out in short order. Our boss is some boss. Old MacArthur scares the living daylights out of all his staff and 'most everyone else."

"Dr MacArthur frightens people? He couldn't. He's a pet. He said I could come and see you this evening and to-morrow and told me I must eat good meals and keep regular hours."

He gaped at me. "You've seen MacArthur? When?"

"Just before I came in here. I had to see him to get permission to visit you, as it's not a visiting day, and late."

"Did you ask to see him?" I nodded. "How did you know he existed? How did you know this place existed? And how did you know I was here?" He lay back on his many pillows. "You've got quite a bit of explaining to do, one way and another, woman."

"Have I?" I pushed the locker over the edge of the room and onto the garden path immediately beyond to keep him quiet. "When it comes to having to explain things," I went on as I sat down, "I'm a non-starter compared with you. Do you realize the trouble you've given me, Joe? Do you, my good man, realize that I've come across country from the camp to-day? That I've had to see every one from Matron at our hospital to this little boss of yours to get in here? And that if it had not been for my Uncle Michael I wouldn't be here at all?"

"Where the devil does Uncle Michael come into it?"

"He's square one. He wrote to ask Sir Thomas Lomax about you, and——"

He cut me short. "He did WHAT?"

"Joe. Relax." I waved him back anxiously. "Please. You'll shoot a temperature if you bounce about like that. If you'll just sit quietly and listen I'll tell you all."

He grinned and relaxed obediently. "Just call me Sealed Lips Slaney. Think I ought to have a pipe as well?" He folded his arms. "I'm listening. On with your tale, woman."

I removed my pork-pie hat and smiled at him. "It won't take long." For the second time that evening I explained about my leave and the journey I had just taken. "Directly Matron gave me that forty-eight I got moving."

He asked carefully, "And you just wrote to your Uncle Michael?"

"Yes."

"And he just wrote to 'Lungs' Lomax?"

"Yes."

"And you just asked for MacArthur, and he let you in?"

"Yes."

He considered me calmly. "Would you mind telling me how you reached this mountain-top? Did you perhaps borrow a tank from the Army?"

166

"No. A bike. A nice dame at the Y.W. lent me hers."

"You came up these hills on a bike?"

"I didn't ride up, obviously. I pushed up and sailed down. It was quite pleasant."

"It was, eh? And you were on duty last night?"

I said, "If you are going to tell me I should have stopped for a square meal and a long sleep let me save you your breath. Dr MacArthur has already given me a stern warning on the consequences of neglecting the needs of the human body. You don't have to give that another thought. I've got dinner lined up here and a bed booked at the Y.W. for when I get back."

He unfolded his arms and refolded them again. He was wearing blue cotton pyjamas; the colour suited his eyes, but the thin material exposed the angular lines of his chest and arms. He might look more rested, but he was still as thin as ever, and, despite all the fresh air, there was no trace of colour in his face. He looked like a charcoal etching to which the artist had decided to add splashes of blue. He lay as still as a figure in a picture, as he asked quietly, "Clare, why?"

I had been expecting and previously dreading that question. Ever since I had discovered where he was I had known that I would have to answer it; I had not known how I was going to answer it. I had pushed the thought to the back of my mind, as something to be faced only when the moment arrived; I had been half afraid, as Mary had also feared, that my upbringing would prove too great a barrier, and that the excellent and inhibiting middle-class principles that had been instilled in me since birth would force me to give a hypocritical if civilized answer. Now the moment had come it never occurred to me to be either hypocritical or shy.

I said, "Because I wanted to see you."

"And why would you want to do that?" he asked drily. "When you never gave one damn about seeing me when I was within range? Does a man have to take to his sick bed before he can register with you, Clare? Or would you perhaps just be feeling sorry for that poor bastard Slaney? Poor old Joe. On his back for the duration. Why not sacrifice a forty-eight for him? Any noble, pure woman would do the same! Is that why you're here?" His voice was growing bitter. "Would that be it? Have you just come to boost my morale and tell me you hope we'll always be good friends? Because if that's what's in your mind, woman—and, knowing you, I'll wager it is—will you object if I ask you to get right back on that bike and go back to your bed at the Y.W.? It's not"—his voice shook suddenly—"that I'm not grateful to you. It's not that I'm not glad to see you again. It's none of those things."

"Then—what is it?" My words fell like stones between us.

"Didn't I tell you that evening I rang you from here? Didn't I tell you that I don't want your pity? Didn't I tell you that I wanted to be left alone? Oh, I know I must sound a perfect heel saying all this to you after the trouble you've taken when you're dog-tired—and you look dog-tired, my—Clare. But won't you understand, woman?—I didn't want to see you—I didn't want you to come—I didn't want anything more to do with you. And I don't. Not now."

I locked my hands in my lap. I had to do that to stop them from shaking. I saw by the way he was gripping his arms that his hands were giving him trouble. "Joe. It's not that I won't understand. I can't understand. Why? Why all this?"

"Why?" He almost spat the word at me. "Why? Damn you, Clare! You must know quite well why! You can't be that dumb! Not even you. I have told you I love you; you must know I still love you like hell, and there's not one damned thing I can do about it, except thank Heaven fasting that you never got to loving me; at least you aren't involved in this— this—waste of time. Do you think love is something you can turn off like a tap? Do you think one can stop loving a person to order? Just because that person is out of sight? Do you think all you have to do is concentrate on a good book? Is that what you think?" he demanded. "For the record, let me tell you, you're wrong. So now—now do you see—why? Now do you understand that if you want to be kind—hell, I know you do—well, the kindest thing you can do for me is to get the hell out of here and out of my life—and stay out."

The violence in his tone soothed me. I said, "No."

He glared at me; his eyes were like blue fire, at last he had some colour in his face. "What do you mean—no?"

"What I say. I'm not getting the hell out of anywhere. Not until my forty-eight is over."

"Are you trying to humour me?" He looked as if he could gladly throw something at me. "I'm in no mood to be humoured."

"I can see that. Calm down, Joe. You're getting too worked up. It won't do your chest any good."

"Did you expect me not to get worked up? And you turning up like this? What am I made of? Solid wood?"

"I don't know what you're made of. I'm not too sure about myself. I'm beginning to get some idea." I stood up. My cap fell to the floor, and I left it there. "You've asked me why I'm here. I said, because I wanted to see you. You've given me a lot of reasons for wanting to see you. None of them have been right. You've said your piece. Supposing you let me say mine."

He watched me as I came closer to his bed. "I'm sorry." He sounded utterly defeated. "Go ahead. Get it over."

I smiled slightly. I was not nervous, or shy. Now, at last, I knew exactly what to say. I was only amused at the contrast between reality and the vague scene with some nebulous young man which, like every young woman, I had visualized in imagination a score of times. "It won't take me long. I may not say it right, as this is something I've not said before, and I'm not sure of the form. I've come to see you, Joe, because I want to ask you to marry me. Will you?"

The colour ebbed from his face. "What was that you said?"

"I asked you to marry me. Will you? When you get well?"

His hands released their grip on his arms and came towards me. Then he realized what he was doing and refolded his arms tightly. "Clare Dillon. Have you taken leave of your senses? Is this some kind of a joke?"

"Do you imagine I've come all this way for a good laugh? No. It isn't."

"You want—to—marry—me?" He looked and sounded shocked.

"Yes."

"In Heaven's name—why? You don't love me at all. You never have."

I said, "Just how do you know that, when you've never bothered to ask?"

"Are you telling me that you do? Clare—no."

"Joe—yes. I do."

The room was suddenly full of silence as well as air. In the silence we looked at each other without moving.

Joe broke the silence. "You must be out of your mind." He nodded to himself as if he had come to the only reasonable answer. "You're on nights—you're tired—you've had a lot of worry—and you've worked yourself into a state where you can believe anything. You can't really be expected to know what you're saying. You can't have suddenly got round to loving me, on your own, with me a hundred miles away."

"I know your body has been a hundred odd miles away. I also know you've been with me—all the time. And don't waste breath telling me you haven't been thinking of me. I won't believe you. You'll just have to stop not believing me. I can't explain how this has happened; I can only tell you that it has. I only realized it that evening you rang to tell me about this. I never knew it when you were around the camp; I never knew or understood anything about you or myself until that evening. Then I knew—and I had to find you. I had to come and see you. I had to tell you. I did not know what sort of a reception I'd get. I had a nasty feeling it would be rather like the one you've given me. I didn't dare brood on that; I didn't brood on what I'd say to you when I got here. I hoped I'd find the words. I have. If you don't like them I'm sorry. And if you don't want to see me I'm sorry. I'm sorry because I'm going to come again. Again and again. It won't be the slightest good your trying to bully me off. I don't get bullied easily."

He pushed his hand through his hair. "It's no use, Clare. This doesn't make sense. You can't possibly feel as you say. You're only saying it because you're sorry——"

"Good God, man! If you tell me I'm only doing this, that, or the other because I'm sorry for you again I'll shake you! Ill as you are, I will! Of course I'm sorry for you! I'm sorry for me, too! Not because you've got tubercle and everything has got to hang up until you're well, but because I can't help loving you, and I know I'm going to marry you, and I know you're going to lead me a hell of a life when we're married! You'll never stop talking; you'll never stop making tea; and you'll spend both our lives telling me what you think I ought to be thinking and feeling, instead of asking me what I think and feel! Men!" I was furious. "Men drive me crazy! I would never dream of trying to fathom a man's mind; why in the name of goodness do men keep nattering on as if they can understand a woman's mind? You'll never do it, Joe! You'll never know what makes me tick, any more than I'll ever know what makes you tick! Here you are, beefing on about my pitying you and being noble and this and that! What do you think I'm made of?" I demanded quite as wildly as he had done. "Solid wood too? Hasn't it struck you that your vanishing might have hurt me? Let me tell you, it's been sheer murder. Nothing less. I know you did it with the best of intentions—but—oh, my darling—Joe"—my anger vanished and I half sobbed at the expression on his face—"don't ever do anything like that again. Please. I can chase over half England; I can chug up hills and borrow bikes; I can bother Army specialists—once. I can't keep on doing those things. Someone'll get narked if I do. There is a war on, my love."

For perhaps half a minute he said nothing. Then he reached for one of my hands and held it in both of his. "Well, now," his voice was very deep, "do you tell me it's still going on? Without the two of us?" His grip tightened. "You said you didn't know the form. I don't either. What do I say?"

"What do you want to say?"

He smiled. "That you're a damned fool of a wonderful girl, and why you should bother to think of waiting around until I can get off my back I'll never be able to understand."

"You do believe me?"

170

"If I say I don't you'll knock my back teeth down my throat. Isn't that true, my darling?"

I grinned. "Probably."

"And you a nurse! And I a poor sick man! Shocking. I'd not have thought it of you, sweetheart." He grew more serious. "There's a lot I'd not have thought of you; there's a lot I don't know about you. In fact, there's precious little I do know. I never guessed, or would have dared to guess, that you would ever come to feel this way about me. I thought you loathed the sight of me?"

"I did. For quite a long time. You used to infuriate me." I put my free hand on top of his and we smiled at each other. "You only do that occasionally now. But you're right about there being a lot more you don't know. There's something else I want to tell you."

"Would it be the number of children we are going to have? And their names? I don't doubt you've that taped too."

"Not yet."

"My darling girl, you're slipping."

"Sorry. Listen." I told him of my plans for my immediate future. "I'm going to get moving on it after this leave. I'm taking your advice, remember? Can I pay you a greater compliment?"

He said slowly, "Wouldn't you say you've paid me the greatest possible already? I would. Incidentally, did you remember it's a Leap Year?"

"So it is."

"You wouldn't have cared if it wasn't?"

"Good gracious, no! After all, Joe, we had to get this straight, and you'd never have asked me. Now would you?"

He shook his head. "No. How could I?"

"I suppose not—being a man. Men are so silly at times."

"Not to worry, dearest. They marry women. That evens it up. Tell me more about this training scheme. What really made you decide?"

I explained briefly.

My explanation worried him. "I had no idea life was so hot in the camp now. The quicker you shift out of there the better. I don't cherish the notion of your being Jerry's target for the night. But there's one snag. You'll be shifting from the camp to London. Wouldn't that be the fire after the frying-pan?"

I shrugged. "Possibly. You mustn't worry about it. Worry is bad for you. You've got to get well, Joe. That's really all that matters."

He said, "Maybe we'll have to do a deal. I'll try and not flap about your war, and you mustn't flap about my bugs. What do you say, sweetheart?"

171

"It's a deal." We shook on it.

"But there's another thing that worries me like hell. No way round that one, either."

"Joe. What is it?"

He looked at me. "I can't kiss you or hold you closer than this. I won't be able to risk it for a long time. Are you going to mind?"

"I'll mind; as you will. We'll survive. We both know what we're in for. It's only until you're well. Have they given you any idea of how long? Or how badly you've got it? And how," I only dared ask then, "are you?"

He smiled as if he appreciated why I had not asked him that last question previously. "Not too bad. Could be a lot worse. That's no line; that's true. Lomax said he thought it would take around three years. Two on my back in here; one taking it easy." His eyes grew troubled again. "It's the devil of a time to keep you waiting, Clare. I'm feeling a heel once more. It's not fair to hold you to this."

I said, "Think how much more of a heel you would have felt if you had turned down my offer."

He smiled faintly. "No gentleman would do that, eh?"

"Not possibly."

"Darling Clare. Dear Heart—are you sure? Are you quite, quite sure?"

"I'm sure. And you?"

He said, "I have been for months now. I was sure the first morning I saw you in the Ob. Block. I told you that. I didn't tell you that when I left you I knew I was only going to be half alive without you. And when I was ill," he went on, "at first I hoped it would simplify things. I had to do without you, and being ill dotted the 'i's' and crossed the 't's'. Then I discovered being ill did nothing of the sort; it just added to the general hell. I've loathed and detested every part of the War, but once I had to opt out, and was here all safe and sound and cosseted like a baby, I would have given my right hand to get back into that ruddy uniform, and back into doing things and not having them done for me. I haven't enjoyed having my war as reading matter with my breakfast egg, Clare; and I haven't enjoyed knowing you and the others were up to your ears in it while I was just dead wood. I tell you, I could kick myself from here to Kingdom Come for picking up this damned bug. And I tell you, I have missed you so, my darling. I've missed you every moment of the day, and the devil of a lot of moments of the night. It's so quiet here. There's nothing but the wind on the trees, and maybe an owl." He stopped momentarily, as if he was too tired to go on.

I said, "Joe, rest a bit. There's plenty of time——"

He shook his head. "Would you bet on that?" And I let him continue. "When you came in with Sister this evening I saw you and knew that subconsciously I had been hoping and praying that you would come. I saw you and—for a moment—the darkness disappeared. You ask me if I'm sure? I'm so sure that I'm not even scared any more. Oh, yes, I've been good and scared; of not seeing you again; of your being killed or mutilated; of your picking up some sort of bug. I've run through the lot. I've even got to flapping about myself. I've no wish to die; never had. I know the score about me on paper; damn it, that's my job. I also know that what a man needs with this bug is something to hang on to, something to keep his eyes on, and until you came in this evening there was nothing for me to keep my eyes on but those trees. I'll tell you this," he added gently, "I'll not need to talk the night nurse into showing me my chart in the morning. I can say now, before the night starts, I'll have the best night I've ever had in this place yet. I'll have you to thank for that sleep, and so much else. So you tell me—how do I start thanking you?"

"You don't do anything so foolish. Let me have my hands."

He let me go immediately. "Have you got to be going? Perhaps you had better. It'll be dusk soon. You oughtn't to ride back in the dark alone."

I laughed at him. "Dear Joe. May I remind you that I reside in the heart of a camp filled with a couple of hundred thousand brutal soldiers who couldn't be more chivalrous? You really don't have to worry about me alone in the dark—on a bike!"

He smiled, reluctantly. "Maybe not. I still don't like it."

I explained I was only going to bring the locker in from the garden. I pushed it by his bed. "It is getting cooler, and I want to sit down. I shan't go until they throw me out. Let's sit and watch the gloaming hand-in-hand and pretend we're an old married couple. Real Darby and Joan types."

He took my hand and I sat down by him. "Do you think that day'll ever come? There are a few snags in the way."

"There are." I looked at the wood ahead. The pines looked feathery in the soft evening light, and threw long, pale shadows on the clearing between them and the hospital. "Let's face them as they come. They aren't worth worrying about. We only live one day at a time. This has been such a good day. Let's not spoil it by wondering about the day after to-morrow. We aren't doing too badly, Joe. We've had to-day, and we have got to-morrow."

He stroked my hair, then tilted my face towards him. He was smiling down at me. His face was illuminated with the same happiness I had glimpsed when I first appeared in his room; this time the light did not fade from his eyes. "This has been more than a good day, my darling. This has been the finest day any man ever lived. And you're right; we've still got to-morrow. What in hell have we got to worry about, sweetheart? Not one ruddy thing," said Joe softly, "not one ruddy thing."

THE END

MY FRIEND THE PROFESSOR
by Lucilla Andrews

Frances Dorland was coping with all the physical and emotional problems of a young probationer nurse when she first met her friend, the professor. A gentle, quiet man, he was to prove a loyal and undemanding friend throughout the pressures and demands of her training life.

It was not until her dearest friend, Estelle, was fighting for her life on the dangerously ill list, that she discovered the truth about Mr Slane, her friend the professor.

0 552 08719 X   £1.75

HOSPITAL CIRCLES
by Lucilla Andrews

Jo Dungarven had all the qualities necessary for a first class nurse. She was kind, cheerful, sensitive, and nearly always good in an emergency. She was also, on occasion, downright foolish. She had a lot of growing up to do.

But third year nurses in a busy London hospital tend to grow up very quickly. When Jo was sent to nurse a dangerously ill young man, she forgot the first rule of hospital life — to keep emotions separate from nursing. It took a great deal of heartache, and several months of gruelling — sometimes tragic — work, before she discovered that at last she had achieved maturity.

0 552 09505 2   £1.75

A SELECTED LIST OF FINE NOVELS
AVAILABLE FROM CORGI BOOKS

WHILE EVERY EFFORT IS MADE TO KEEP PRICES LOW, IT IS SOMETIMES NECESSARY TO INCREASE PRICES AT SHORT NOTICE. CORGI BOOKS RESERVE THE RIGHT TO SHOW NEW RETAIL PRICES ON COVERS WHICH MAY DIFFER FROM THOSE PREVIOUSLY ADVERTISED IN THE TEXT OR ELSEWHERE.

THE PRICES SHOWN BELOW WERE CORRECT AT THE TIME OF GOING TO PRESS (MAY '86).

All these books are available at your book shop or newsagent, or can be ordered direct from the publisher. Just tick the titles you want and fill in the form below.

CORGI BOOKS, Cash Sales Department, P.O. Box 11, Falmouth, Cornwall.

Please send cheque or postal order, no currency.

Please allow cost of book(s) plus the following for postage and packing:

U.K. Customers—Allow 55p for the first book, 22p for the second book and 14p for each additional book ordered, to a maximum charge of £1.75.

B.F.P.O. and Eire—Allow 55p for the first book, 22p for the second book plus 14p per copy for the next seven books, thereafter 8p per book.

Overseas Customers—Allow £1.00 for the first book and 25p per copy for each additional book.

NAME (Block Letters) ....

ADDRESS ....

....